D1097127

THYSSEN-BORNEMISZA COLLECTION
CATALOGUE OF THE EXHIBITED WORKS OF ART

prepared by

Gertrude Borghero

Villa Favorita, Castagnola 1981

English translation: F. Superbi / M.T. & J. Hodgson

Printed in Switzerland
by
Società d'arti grafiche
già Veladini & Co. SA, Lugano

CONTENTS

Cover: cat. no. 218 - Momper
View of a Port with Motifs of Rome

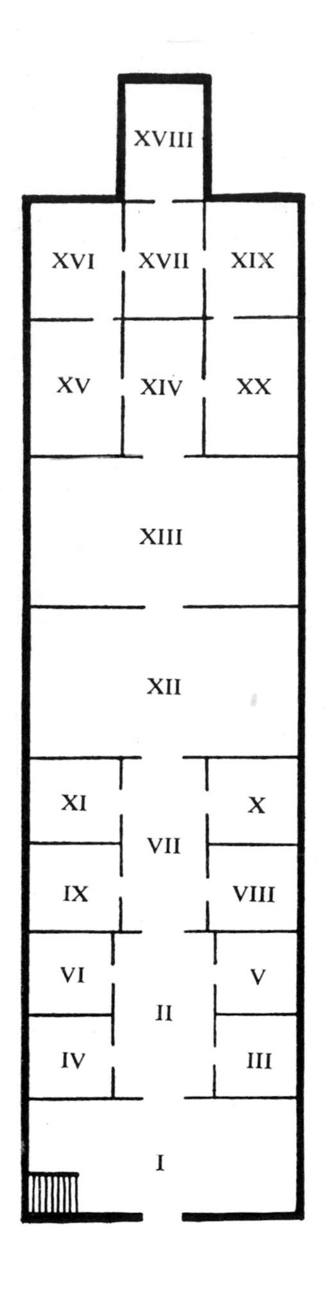

XVIII	French masters of the XVII and XVIII century.
XIX	French and Italian painting of the XVII century. Sculptures by Houdon.
XVII	Venetian masters of the XVIII century.
XVI	Italian High and Late Renaissance.
XX	Spanish painting, XVI to XVIII century.
XV	Italian High Renaissance.
XIV	International Gothic and Early Renaissance.
XIII	Venetian masterpieces of the XVI century. Italian Baroque sculptures and furniture.
XII	Dutch and Flemish masterpieces of the XVII century.
XI	Dutch genre painting, XVII century.
X	Dutch landscape painting, XVII century.
IX	Dutch interior and still-life painting, XVII century.
VIII	Rembrandt and his circle.
VII	Dutch and Flemish painting from Mannerism to Baroque.
VI	Dutch painting, XV century.
V	Flemish masters of the XV century.
IV	Lukas and Hans Cranach and Old German portrait painting around 1550.
III	German Renaissance (Bavaria and Donauschule).
II	Old German panel painting 1450-1520.
I	Italian panel painting, XIII to XIV century. French and Italian sculpture, XIII to XVI century and ivory reliefs.

PRACTICAL GUIDE

The exhibited paintings are catalogued in numerical order.

Sculptures and other art objects are listed in numerical order, preceded by a 'K', at the end of the catalogue.

Opening times:

Good Friday to second Sunday of October
Friday to Saturday 10-12 and 2-5
Sundays 2-5

Entrance: Fr. 7.--
Students (with card) and 10-17 year olds: Fr. 3.--
Groups of 20 or more: Fr. 3.50

The following catalogues are also obtainable:

Thyssen-Bornemisza Collection 2 volumes (text and illustrations) in German and English	Fr. 140.--
Some Renaissance Pictures in the Thyssen-Bornemisza Collection (illustrated catalogue including 24 colour reproductions) text German-English	Fr. 50.--
The Oriental Carpets in the Thyssen-Bornemisza Collection (with 18 colour reproductions) in German and English	Fr. 60.--

FOREWORD

The Thyssen-Bornemisza Collection has so far been the work of two generations. It was begun in the nineteen-twenties by Baron Heinrich Thyssen-Bornemisza (1875-1947), whose intention was to create a panorama of European painting from the fourteenth to the eighteenth century by means of works of prime significance. He acquired the Villa Favorita in 1932, and between 1933 and 1937 had the gallery constructed, building it on to the already standing Glorietta. In this way the collection, which until then had been housed in Hungary, received its present setting.
After his demise his son, Baron Hans Heinrich Thyssen-Bornemisza, the present proprietor, opened the gallery to the public at Easter 1948. He then set about the task of completing his father's collection as well as expanding it to include sectors previously excluded, such as European and American painting of the nineteenth and twentieth centuries, which constantly enriches and transforms the collection. These periods, however, are not referred to in this catalogue as the paintings themselves cannot be exhibited here owing to lack of space.
The new edition of this catalogue is by no means designed to be a scientific instrument, but rather a means of providing information and help for the visitor to the gallery, who will nevertheless still find, where possible, information based on the latest research. This new version is due to the untiring efforts of Gertrude Borghero, the Collection's librarian. Furthermore, I wish to express my gratitude to Hanna Kiel, Marco Grassi and Irene Gernsheim for their contribution in the preparation of this catalogue.

Simon de Pury
Curator

January 1981

ALTDORFER, Albrecht.

* around 1480 probably in Regensburg + 1538 in Regensburg.
He was the leading master of the 'Donauschule', a style of landscape painting to which Lucas Cranach the Elder, Jörg Breu the Elder and Rueland Frueauf also belonged. His predilection for vivid colours and light effects gave him an almost equivalent standing as the one held amongst painters of his time by Matthias Grünewald.

1 PORTRAIT OF A YOUNG WOMAN.
Pine, 59 × 45.2 cm.

This portrait of around 1520 was considered the only surviving portrait by Altdorfer until in 1967 a male portrait was discovered in a private Swiss collection, which, according to several scholars, is to be accepted as a work by the artist.

AMBERGER, Christoph.

* around 1500 in Swabia + 1562 in Augsburg.
The influence of Hans Burgkmair, the Augsburg master, (cf. cat. no. 49) and of the Venetian portraitists is particularly apparent in his early work. Later Amberger took as his artistic model Hans Holbein the Younger, whose pictorial perfection he comes close to in his portraits.

2 PORTRAIT OF MATTHEUS SCHWARZ THE ELDER.
Pine, 74 × 61.5 cm.

The man represented was an important employee in the service of the Fuggers. His horoscope with the year 1542, the date of the portrait, appears in the view through the window.
Provenance: Leopold Hirsch Collection, London.

ANGELICO, Fra Giovanni da Fiesole, called Beato Angelico.

* around 1400 at Vicchio in the Mugello + 1455 in Rome.
He is documented in the convent of San Domenico at Fiesole from 1420. His artistic development reveals the influence of Lorenzo Monaco. His clear, delicate and precise way of painting combines the Giottesque style of the followers of Gaddi and the Gothic elegance of Simone Martini. But he was also responsive to the innovations of his contemporaries, Ghiberti, Brunelleschi, Michelozzo and Donatello.

3 MADONNA ENTHRONED WITH ANGELS.
Poplar, 100 × 49 cm.

The composition and the music-making angels betray the strong influence of Masaccio, particularly of his 'Pisan Madonna' now in London.
Provenance: Pierpont Morgan Library, New York.

ANTONELLO DA MESSINA.

* 1430 in Messina + 1479 in Messina.
In Naples he was a pupil of Colantonio, from whom he took the technique of oil painting, new for Italy, and the great admiration for Flemish painters, particularly for the van Eyck brothers, Petrus Christus and Rogier van der Weyden. As a portraitist he led the way for Italian painters.

4 PORTRAIT OF A MAN.
Wood, 27.5 × 21 cm.
Signed on the stone ledge: 'Antonellus Messanus pinx'.

The portrait betrays the typical characteristics of Antonello's portraits: the strong oval of the face stands out from the dark background, the piercing eyes are directed towards the observer.
Provenance: Sir George Houston Boswall
of Calderhaugh Collection, Scotland.

APT, Ulrich the Elder.

The workshop of the Apt family played a leading role in Augsburg, as did those of Hans Holbein the Elder and Hans Burgkmair. Four members of the family are recorded in documents as painters: Ulrich Apt the Elder (master in 1481, died in 1532), his son Jacob Apt (master in 1510, died in 1518), Ulrich Apt the Younger (documented in Augsburg until 1520, died in 1533) and Michael Apt (master in 1520, in Augsburg until 1527).

5 THE LAMENTATION OF CHRIST.
Pine, 44 × 35.5 cm.

A predilection for details, sparkling colours and a slightly old-fashioned but nevertheless thorough and precise technique, typical characteristics of the Apt workshop, are also to be found in this work.

ASPERTINI, Amico.

* around 1474 probably in Bologna + 1552 in Bologna.
After an apprenticeship with his father, he worked with Ercole de' Roberti, Lorenzo Costa and Francesco Francia. He is a versatile artist, whose works often contain a touch of irony and even melancholy.

6 PORTRAIT OF TOMMASO RAIMONDI.
Poplar, 41.5 × 32.5 cm.

The attribution to Aspertini is due to van Marle.
Provenance: Van Stolk Collection, The Hague.

AST, Balthasar van der.

* around 1593 in Middelburg + 1657 in Delft.
He was a pupil of his brother-in-law Ambrosius Bosschaert and was active in Bergen op Zoom, Utrecht and Delft. Like Bosschaert he specialized in still lifes with flowers and fruit, but his compositions are more animated and his technique richer in tone and more plastic.

7 STILL LIFE WITH VASE, FLOWERS, SHELLS AND INSECTS.
Oak, 51.5 × 35 cm.
Signed and dated on the lower right: 'Balthasar van der Ast 1628'.

BAEGERT, Derick.

* around 1440 in Wesel + 1515 in Wesel.
It is only on account of recent research that a considerable number of paintings that were formerly attributed to Duenwege, have been ascribed to Baegert. An important representative of the German Late Gothic period, he combined influences from Westphalia, the Netherlands and Cologne into his own personal style, which reminds one of Martin Schongauer.

FIVE FRAGMENTS OF A 'CRUCIFIXION' ALTARPIECE.

Originally a large oak panel of approximately 215 × 400 cm, it was painted in 1477, probably for the church of Matena in Wesel. During an iconoclasm the altarpiece was removed from its place and totally dismembered. The following five fragments have been reunited in the collection:

9 SAINT VERONICA AND A GROUP OF HORSEMEN.
Lower left part.
113 × 97.5 cm.

Provenance: Edward Eyre Collection, London.

10 CHRIST CARRYING THE CROSS.
Upper left part.
87 × 98 cm.

Above and to the left traces of the original border.
Provenance: American Private Collection.

11 THE GOOD CENTURION AT THE FOOT OF THE CROSS.
Upper central part.
82 × 52.5 cm.

On the border, to the left, part of the figure of Christ is visible; to the right, part of the bad thief.
Provenance: Lord Marchamley Collection, England.

12 MARY MAGDALENE KNEELING AT THE FOOT OF THE CROSS.
Lower central part.
80 × 42.5 cm.

Provenance: Dr Weiskorn Collection, Bonn.

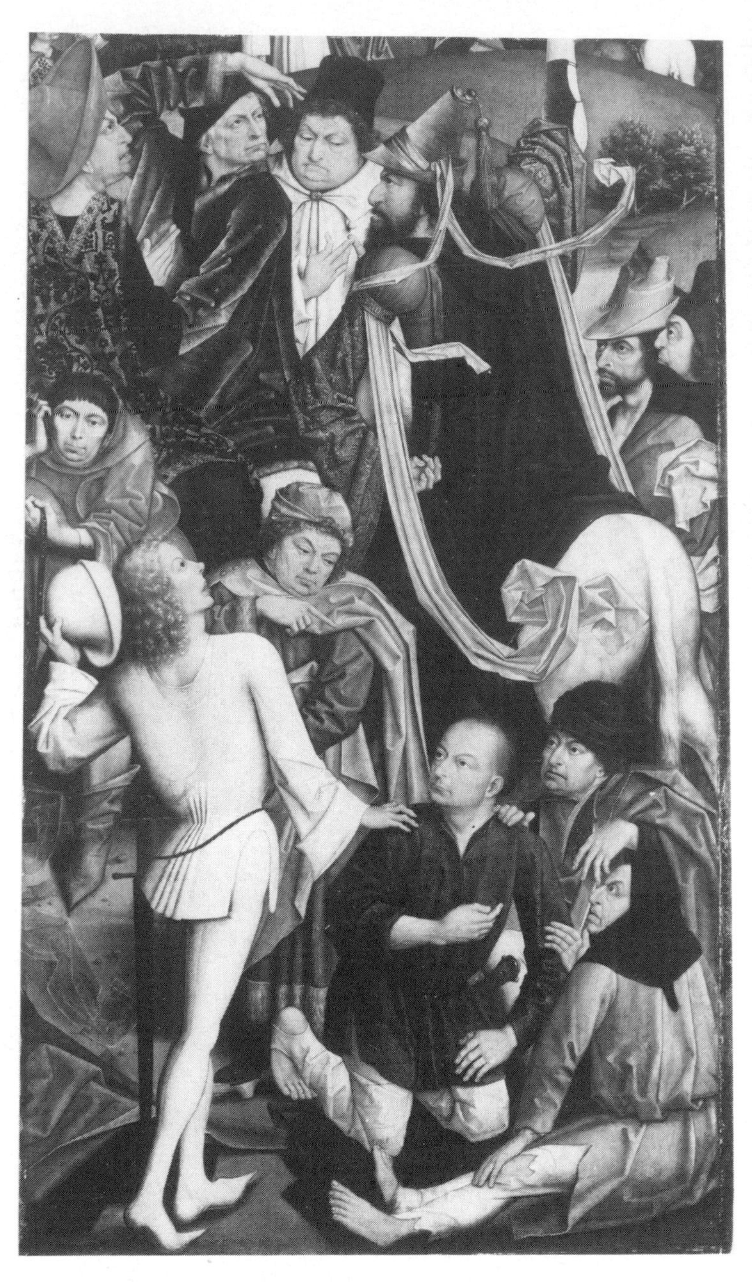

13 THE GOOD CENTURION AND SOLDIERS CASTING LOTS FOR CHRIST'S RAIMENT.
Lower right part.
159 × 92.5 cm.

Provenance: Duke of Norfolk Collection, Arundel Castle.

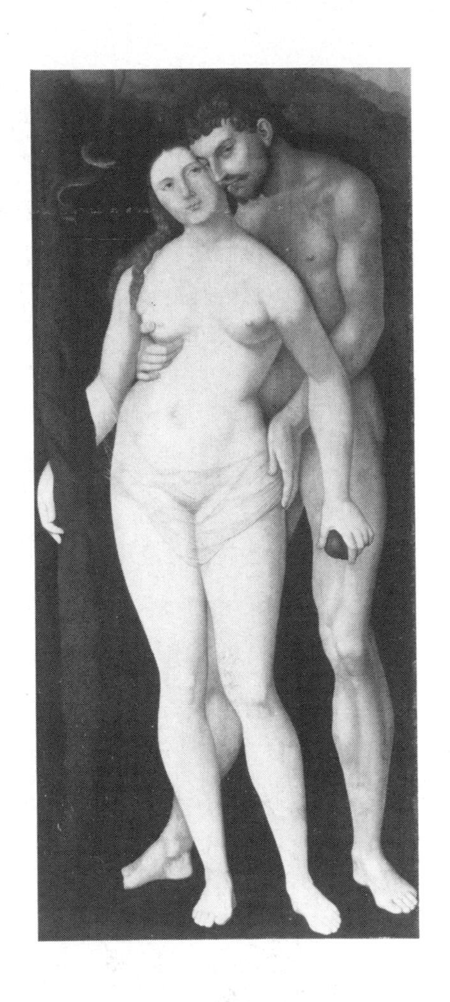

BALDUNG, Hans, called Grien.

* 1484 or 1485 in Schwäbisch-Gmünd + 1545 in Strasbourg. Together with Grünewald, Dürer, Cranach the Elder, Altdorfer and Holbein the Younger he is one of the great creative talents whose works led to the first decades of the sixteenth century becoming one of the golden ages of German painting. He was Dürer's most gifted pupil.

14 ADAM AND EVE.
Pine, 148 × 67.4 cm.
Signed on the bole of the tree to the left: 'HGB'.

The nude, a still recent subject matter in painting, corresponded to Grien's humanistic ideals of beauty and never failed to attract him. This work belongs to his late period and is to be dated around 1538.
Provenance: Baron Bissing Collection, Munich.

15 PORTRAIT OF A LADY.
Pine, 68 × 51.5 cm.
Signed and dated on the lower left: 'HB 1530'.

This portrait reveals the influence of Lucas Cranach the Elder, whose 'Salomé' in the Budapest Museum may have served as a model.
Provenance: Count Dumoulin-Eckert Collection, Munich.

BARTOLO DI FREDI.

* around 1330 in Siena + 1409 in Siena.
A typical representative of Sienese painting of the second half of the fourteenth century, Bartolo di Fredi continued the tradition of Simone Martini and the Lorenzetti brothers, becoming at the same time the most important mediator between these great predecessors and the generation of artists that followed him. On his death his son, Andrea di Bartolo, took over his workshop.

16 THE WAY TO GOLGOTHA.
Poplar, 54.5 × 49 cm.

This panel is part of a predella of which the central panel representing the 'Crucifixion' is now in the Metropolitan Museum in New York. The 'Lamentation' in the Museum in Stockholm and the 'Resurrection' in the Walters Art Gallery in Baltimore also belong to the same predella.
Provenance: Baron Heinrich von Tucher Collection, Lindau.

FRA BARTOLOMEO, called Baccio della Porta.

* 1472 in Florence + 1517 in the Dominican convent of Santa Maria Maddalena in Pian di Mugnone near Florence.
Under the influence of Savonarola, in 1496 he burnt his profane paintings and drawings, and in 1500 he entered the Dominican Order. Inspired by the art of the fifteenth century, Fra Bartolomeo brought the painting of altarpieces to its highest form of expression in Florence. He was influenced by Leonardo, Raphael and Michelangelo, and his paintings express his deep religiousness.

17 HOLY FAMILY WITH INFANT SAINT JOHN.
Poplar, 62 × 47 cm.

The figures right in the foreground frame a lush, open landscape which creates a poetic atmosphere around the Holy Family, revealing the painter's deep feeling for nature. An early work by the master, datable between 1505 and 1506.
Provenance: Philip Vos Collection, Sussex.

BARTOLOMEO VENETO.

Venetian painter of the first half of the sixteenth century.
In his earliest known work, a 'Madonna and Child', he indicated next to his signature that he was half Venetian and half Cremonese. His early works betray the influence of Giovanni Bellini; later he approaches the style of Andrea Solario. In his portraits he chooses Antonello as his model.

18 MADONNA AND CHILD.
Poplar, 45 × 33.3 cm.

This painting may be dated between 1515 and 1520.

19 PORTRAIT OF A PATRICIAN.
Poplar, 87.3 × 59 cm.

In the second decade of the sixteenth century Bartolomeo Veneto dedicated himself in particular to portraits, which are among his best paintings. Strong modelling and precision of drawing together with elegance and richness in the costumes make him a worthy follower of Antonello da Messina. This portrait, considered a late work, is datable between 1525 and 1530.
Provenance: Baron Heinrich von Tucher Collection, Lindau.

BASSANO, Jacopo. (Jacopo da Ponte)

* around 1515 in Bassano + 1593 in Bassano.
He first studied painting with his father at Bassano and after 1530 with Bonifazio Veronese in Venice. In 1541 he returned to his native town where he founded an active workshop. His style was influenced by Lorenzo Lotto, Titian and Parmigianino. Inspired by the surrounding landscape he created a new kind of genre painting, becoming the leading landscape-painter in sixteenth century Italy.

20 PASTORAL SCENE.
Canvas, 140 × 119.5 cm.

This picture is one of the earliest examples of genre painting in Italy and proves that Jacopo and not his son Francesco was the initiator of this new style. It is datable around 1560.
Provenance: Earl of Harewood Collection, Yorkshire.

BEHAM, Barthel.

* 1502 in Nuremberg + 1540 in Bologna, on a journey.
In 1525 he was involved in social and religious unrest and was expelled from Nuremberg. He settled in Munich, where he entered the service of Duke William IV of Bavaria as court painter. Beham continued the classical style of Dürer, modified by the influence of Venetian masters.

23 PORTRAIT OF A FEMALE MEMBER OF THE STÜPF FAMILY.

24 PORTRAIT OF A MALE MEMBER OF THE STÜPF FAMILY.
Pine, 67.3 × 50.3 cm.

Both signed and dated on the upper right: 'BBP 1528'.

The portraits are influenced by Dürer's clear, realistic late style. The plastic modelling of the faces and the vivid colours confer a monumental effect on these works.

BELLINI, Gentile.

* around 1429 in Venice + 1507 in Venice.
Pupil of his father Jacopo, he was influenced by his brother-in-law Andrea Mantegna. In 1479, as the leading portrait painter of his time, he was sent by the Venetian Senate to Constantinople, to Sultan Mahomet II. In his descriptive compositions he appears to anticipate Carpaccio.

25 ANNUNCIATION.
Poplar, 134 × 125 cm.

This painting has been attributed to various masters: formerly it was thought to be the work of Domenico Morone. Berenson ascribed it to Jacopo da Montagnana and Hendy considered it the work of Giovanni Bellini. The most convincing attribution to Gentile Bellini made by Longhi is confirmed by comparing it with the 'Madonna with two Donors' in the Berlin Museum and the 'Blessed Lorenzo Giustiniani' of 1465, two early works by Gentile.

BELLINI, Jacopo.

* around 1400 in Venice + around 1470-1471 in Venice.
Jacopo, the father of Gentile and Giovanni Bellini, was a pupil of Gentile da Fabriano. He worked in Verona, Venice, Ferrara and Padua; however, only a small number of his works have survived. His drawings that are preserved in the Louvre and in the British Museum illustrate his particular creative gift.

25 A SAINT JEROME.
Panel, 40.5 × 30.4 cm.
Signed and dated to the right on the church pillar: '1443 Jacobus Bellini'.

As the earliest of the preserved works of the master, it is still conceived in the Gothic style. The saint is sitting in the centre, in utter solitude, absorbed in reading the Bible. The poetic atmosphere of the landscape anticipates the special quality of Giovanni Bellini's art.
Provenance: Rasini Collection, Milan.

BELLINI, Giovanni.

* around 1430 in Venice + 1516 in Venice.
Brother of Gentile, he was always second to his brother in official recognition although the more gifted painter. Also pupil of his father, Jacopo, and of his brother-in-law, Andrea Mantegna, he appears influenced by Antonello da Messina and, in his later pictures, by Titian. He is the most important artist of the Venetian Renaissance.

26

NUNC DIMITTIS.
Wood, 62 × 82.5 cm.

The painting represents the old prophet Simeon taking the Christ Child in his hands in the Temple with the words: 'Nunc dimittis ...' (Now, my Lord, dismiss your servant, because my eyes have seen the Saviour ...), according to Luke (2,25-30). As the first of the great Venetian landscape painters, Giovanni Bellini chose to represent this scene against the background of a poetical landscape.
Provenance: Count Pourtalès Collection, Paris.

BELLOTTO, Bernardo.

* 1720 in Venice + 1780 in Warsaw.
Pupil and nephew of Antonio Canale, he also used the latter's surname of 'Canaletto'. He worked not only in Venice but also in Rome, Lombardy, Piedmont and Tuscany before being called to Dresden as court painter by August III of Poland in 1746. From 1770 until his death he worked as court painter to King Stanislas Poniatowski in Warsaw.

27 BRIDGE ACROSS THE BRENTA.
Canvas, 48.5 × 73 cm.

The picture was painted between 1744 and 1747, before the painter's activity in Dresden. As well as showing a similarity to Canaletto's late style, the painting also reveals the highly poetical atmosphere typical of Bellotto's vedute.

BERCKHEYDE, Gerrit Adriaensz.

* 1638 in Haarlem + 1698 in Haarlem.
Together with his elder brother Job, he took up the tradition of architectural painting established in Haarlem by Saenredam. He chose his subjects in his own town, in The Hague and in Amsterdam, but among his vast production views of Cologne and of Heidelberg are also to be found. Jan van der Heyden and the Berckheyde brothers are the most significant representatives of Dutch vedute painting.

29 VIEW OF THE BINNENHOF IN THE HAGUE WITH THE RIDDERZAAL.
Canvas, 54 × 63.5 cm.
Signed on the lower left: 'G. Berck Heyde'.

The Ridderzaal, of which the west façade is seen, was built in 1275 under Count Floris V as the enlargement of the Palace of the Counts of Holland. The 'Stadholder's Quarters' on the left was constructed in 1640. Luminous colours with transparent shadows and an extremely accurate design are Berckheyde's main characteristics.
Provenance: Adrian Haye Collection, London.

30 THE NIEUWEZIJDS VOORBURGWAL WITH THE FLOWER-MARKET IN AMSTERDAM.
Canvas, 53.5 × 63.5 cm.
Signed and dated on the lower left: 'Gerrit berck Heyde 1686'.

In 1884 this romantic canal was covered and is today a street. On the right appears the back of the former Town Hall, now the Royal Palace, built between 1648 and 1664 after the design of Jacob van Campen.
Provenance: Sir Francis Cook Collection,
Doughty House, Richmond.

BICCI DI LORENZO.

* 1373 in Florence + 1452 in Arezzo.
Descended from a well-known Florentine family of artists, he worked as an apprentice in the workshop of his father, Lorenzo di Bicci. He was influenced by Agnolo Gaddi, Lorenzo Monaco, Gentile da Fabriano and Fra Angelico. Still rooted in the Late Gothic tradition, he was only superficially influenced by the Renaissance. After his death his son, Neri di Bicci, carried on the workshop.

30 A TRIPTYCH.
Central panel: Crucifixion, 75 × 31 cm.
Side panels: Annunciation, 60 × 30.5 cm.
Gold base, gabled.

According to an old inscription on the back, this triptych was found in the store-room of a building attached to Santa Maria del Fiore in Florence, which was demolished for the enlargement of the Cathedral square.
Provenance: Mrs Peter Sommerwell Collection,
Fettercairn House, Kincardine, Scotland.

PSEUDO-BOCCACCINO.

Bode gave this name to a Lombard painter active in Venice at the beginning of the sixteenth century. His pictures were formerly ascribed to a Cremonese artist, Boccaccio Boccaccino. The works of the Pseudo-Boccaccino reveal influences of Bramantino, Solario and Leonardo da Vinci. The identification of this artist with Agostino da Lodi is doubted.

32 LADON AND SYRINX.

33 PAN AND SYRINX.
Poplar, each panel, 46 × 36.5 cm.

The two panels were probably part of a wedding chest and represent two scenes from the story of Pan and Syrinx, from Ovid's Metamorphoses.
Provenance: R. H. Benson Collection, London.

BOCCATI, Giovanni.

* around 1420 in Camerino (Marches) + around 1480.
In 1445 the painter was given citizenship of Perugia. He created a considerable number of altarpieces for the churches and convents of the town and its environs, which are now partly in the town's art-gallery. His work is significant for the development of quattrocento-painting in Umbria.

33 A SAINT SAVINIUS AND HERMIT SAINT.
Poplar, 27 × 36 cm.

This panel was the left part of the predella of the altarpiece, dated 1473, formerly in the Chapel of San Savino dei Petrangeli in the Cathedral of Orvieto, now in the Budapest Museum.
Provenance: Bequest of Emily Meynell, Church of the
Holy Angels, Hoar Cross, Staffordshire.

BOL, Ferdinand.

* 1616 in Dordrecht + 1680 in Amsterdam.
In 1635 he became a pupil of Rembrandt, and even as an independent painter he maintained for a long time the pictorial technique of his master before he developed his own somewhat pompous style. He was much sought after as a portraitist, and particularly his portrait-groups are masterpieces of the Rembrandt school.

33 C SELF-PORTRAIT.
Canvas, 91 × 78 cm.
Signed on the lower right.

For a long time this portrait was attributed to Rembrandt.
Provenance: Walker Art Collection,
Minneapolis Museum, USA.

BOLTRAFFIO, Giovanni Antonio.

* 1467 in Milan + 1516 in Milan.
Of his life only what is inscribed on his tombstone is known. He was the most gifted pupil of Leonardo da Vinci; it appears, however, that after his apprenticeship he fell back to his earlier style, a fact that has perplexed art critics.

34 PORTRAIT OF A LADY AS SAINT LUCY.
Poplar, 47.5 × 37.5 cm.

After the cleaning of the painting in 1935 the right hand of the woman portrayed reappeared, holding an eye, symbol of her patron saint Lucy. The portrait is to be dated about 1500.
Provenance: Count Febo Borromeo Collection, Milan.

BONFIGLI, Benedetto.

* around 1420 in Perugia + 1496 in Perugia.
The charm and gracefulness of his figures reveal Bonfigli to be a true Umbrian master, although the clear influence of Tuscan painting of the early Renaissance, and particularly of Fra Angelico, Domenico Veneziano, Filippo Lippi and Benozzo Gozzoli are present in his works. His frescoes in the Cappella dei Priori in Perugia, and his altarpieces and murals in churches and convents in the town are among the most representative works of his time, also due to their beautiful background landscapes.

34 A ANNUNCIATION.
Poplar, 51 × 39 cm.

Provenance: Private Collection, Rome.

BOPP, Sebald.

His dates are not known with certainty. Born in Bamberg and trained in Würzburg, he established himself in Nördlingen, where he had an influential workshop and worked for the court of the Margrave of Ansbach. In a document of 1486 the Margravine Sophia of Brandenburg-Ansbach recommended him as a gifted master.

35 WEDDING PORTRAIT OF A LADY WEARING THE ORDER OF THE SWAN.
Pine, 44.5 × 28 cm.

It has not been possible to identify the sitter. She wears the cap as symbol of marriage and the drape worn by unmarried women. The pink in her hand, symbol of fidelity, indicates that a companion piece portraying her husband was originally placed on the left.
Provenance: Benedictine Convent, Admont (Styria).

BORDONE, Paris.

* around 1500 in Treviso + 1571 in Venice.
According to Vasari, Bordone was for a short time pupil of Titian, although throughout his life he had to endure his hostility. He was artistically inspired by Giorgione, Lorenzo Lotto and Pordenone.

36 PORTRAIT OF A YOUNG WOMAN.
Canvas, 101 × 82 cm.

Representations of nymphs, goddesses, courtesans or of opulent women richly dressed in velvet and silk, with hair in curls, predominate in Bordone's late work. This portrait is to be dated around 1555.
Provenance: Earl of Radnor Collection, Longford Castle, Salisbury.

BOSSCHAERT, Ambrosius the Elder.

* 1573 in Antwerp + 1621 in The Hague.
He worked in Middelburg, Bergen op Zoom, Utrecht and Breda and founded a flourishing school of flower still-life painting. His three sons, Ambrosius the Younger, Johannes and Abraham, as well as his brother-in-law Balthasar van der Ast, were among his pupils.

37 VASE WITH FLOWERS.
Copper, 68 × 50 cm.
Signed on the lower left with the monogram 'AB'; on the back, the date 1607.

Bosschaert arranged his beautiful decorative flower bouquets on the basis of the symmetrical composition of various flower studies, painted in a scientific-naturalistic mode. He did not take into consideration the fact that his flowers bloom at different times, and he rearranged the same studies in numerous compositions. The tastefully arranged contrasts of colour tones and the precision of his drawing heighten the decorative effect.
Provenance: J. C. H. Heldring Collection,
Osterbeek, Holland.

BOTTICINI, Francesco.

* 1446 in Florence + 1497 in Florence.
He worked as a pupil of Neri di Bicci and was influenced by Castagno, Cosimo Rosselli, Verrocchio, Botticelli and Filippino Lippi. For this reason some of his best works were for a time attributed to these masters.

38 SAINTS CECILIA, VALERIAN, TIBURTIUS AND FEMALE DONOR.
Poplar, 51 × 43 cm.

Provenance: Dreyfus Collection, Paris.

BOUCHER, François.

* 1703 in Paris + 1770 in Paris.
First a pupil of his father, in 1720 he became a pupil of François Lemoyne. The art of Watteau had a decisive influence on his style. From 1727 to 1730 he lived in Italy, winning the 'Prix de Rome'. In 1734 he became a member of the Academy and as a successful painter he received commissions from Louis XV and Madame de Pompadour. In 1755 he was nominated inspector of the Royal Gobelin tapestry manufactury. In 1763 he was appointed 'First Painter to the King' and Director of the Royal Academy in 1765. From 1736 he painted genre scenes which reveal his particular skill.

39 LA TOILETTE.
Canvas, 52.5 × 66.5 cm.

The first owner of the picture was Count Karl Gustav Tessin, Swedish Ambassador to France, an enthusiastic patron and friend of the artist. Tessin, on Queen Lovisa Ulrike's behalf, ordered from Boucher a series of four pictures representing 'The Hours of the Day of a Fashionable Lady'. Apparently only the 'Morning', now in the Stockholm Museum, was painted. The seated lady, represented fixing her garter, is Madame Boucher, who often posed for her husband.
Provenance: Baron Nathaniel Rothschild Collection, Vienna.

BOUTS, Dieric.

* between 1410 and 1420 in Haarlem + 1475 in Löwen.
Together with Hans Memling, Bouts is one of the great painters who were followers of Rogier van der Weyden. We do not know where and with whom he was apprenticed, but especially in his early works he reveals the influence of Rogier van der Weyden and of Petrus Christus.

41 VIRGIN AND CHILD.
Oak, 28.5 × 20 cm.

As painter of the Virgin, Bouts produced important works; he enriched the traditional versions, intensifying the expression and gesture of the Madonna as well as the proportion of the room or the landscape in the background. The Madonna is here represented in an enclosed garden against a background of the brocade cloth of honour, composition based on the Song of Solomon (4, 12).

BRAMANTE, Donato. (Donato d'Angeli Lazzari)

* 1444 at Monte Asdrualdo in the Duchy of Urbino
+ 1514 in Rome.
He is thought to have been a pupil of Mantegna as well as of Piero della Francesca. In 1477 he established himself in Lombardy and was active in Milan as architect in the service of Lodovico il Moro. He fulfilled his career in Rome as a great renewer of Italian Renaissance architecture.

42 ECCE HOMO.
Poplar, 109 × 73 cm.

The mysterious metaphysical effect of the picture is due to a metallic rigidity in the modelling and to the exceptional precision of the design. On account of its closeness to the 'Christ at the Column' in the Brera Gallery, Milan, the painting has been attributed to Bramante and is dated between 1480 and 1485.
Provenance: Countess Mocenigo-Soranzo Collection, Milan.

BRONZINO, Agnolo. (Agniolo di Cosimo di Mariano)

* 1503 at Monticelli near Florence + 1572 in Florence.
Of Bronzino's teachers, it was Jacopo da Pontormo who influenced him most. Numerous decorations of palaces, churches and public buildings in Florence and in Tuscany were executed in collaboration with Pontormo. As a highly appreciated artist during his lifetime, Bronzino received many commissions, especially from the Medici family.

42 A COSIMO DE' MEDICI IN ARMOUR.
Wood, 76.5 × 59 cm.

Of the different replicas by Bronzino of his famous portrait of Cosimo in the Uffizi in Florence, that in the Thyssen-Bornemisza collection is to be considered one of the finest, due to the masterly handling of the light.

BRUEGHEL, Jan the Elder.

* 1568 in Brussels + 1625 in Antwerp.
Brueghel of the 'Velours' or of the 'Flowers' was the most gifted of the two sons of Pieter Brueghel the Elder and made his name as a painter of still lifes and small landscapes, rendered with subtle brush strokes and presenting a striking richness of detail in a great variety of delicate colours.

42 D CHRIST IN THE TEMPEST.
Copper, 26.5 × 34.5 cm.
Signed and dated on the lower right: 'Brueghel 1596'.

An impressive example of Brueghel's small landscapes, in luminous colours.
Provenance: S. Lodi Collection, Campione d'Italia.

BROUWER, Adriaen.

* 1605 in Oudenaerde + 1638 in Antwerp.
He is documented in Antwerp in 1625; before that he may have been an apprentice of Frans Hals in Haarlem. His early works are based on the naturalism of Peter Brueghel the Elder, but he later increased the impact and depth of his painting by enhancing the contrasts of the chiaroscuro and by a careful choice of his figurative style. His success in entertaining his public through a realistic representation of an unrepressed joy of living, is testified to by his popularity and also by the number of imitators he had.

43 LANDSCAPE WITH DRINKING PEASANTS.
Oak, 63.5 × 97 cm.

This picture is to be dated around 1630, during Brouwer's activity in Antwerp.
Provenance: Dr Singer Collection, Vienna.

BROUWER, Adriaen or his circle.

44 PEASANTS AT THE FIRE-PLACE OF AN INN.
Oak, 34.5 × 27 cm.
Provenance: Georges Giroux Collection, Brussels.

BROUWER, Adriaen, follower.

45 GUITAR-PLAYER.
Oak, 30.5 × 22.5 cm.

Provenance: Sanderson Collection, Edinburgh.

BRUYN, Bartholomäus the Elder.

* 1493 probably in Wesel + 1555 in Cologne.
He created numerous religious works, mainly altarpieces, although portraits were his main subject. Active in Cologne from 1515, he became the leading portrait painter of the local patrician families. He was notably inspired by his older friend Joos van Cleve.

47 A ADORATION OF THE CHRIST CHILD.
Oak, 62.5 × 55.5 cm.

Friedländer dated the panel as belonging to the middle period of the master when his works reflected the influence of Italian Mannerism.
Provenance: Duke of Anhalt-Dessau Collection,
Schloss Wörlitz.

BURGKMAIR, Hans the Elder.

* 1473 in Augsburg + 1531 in Augsburg.
He learned his craft from his father, Thoman Burgkmair, and in 1488 became an apprentice of Martin Schongauer in Colmar. In 1498, after travelling in northern Italy, he took over the workshop of his father with notable success.

49 THE DEPOSITION.
Pine, 66.3 × 118.8 cm.

According to K. Feuchtmayr, it is the predella of the 'Holy Cross Altarpiece', dated 1519, in the Alte Pinakothek in Munich. The coat of arms of the Peutinger family of Augsburg, the probable owners of the painting, appears on the back of 'The Deposition' as well as on the altarpiece.
Provenance: Dr Rothmann Collection, Berlin.

BUTINONE, Bernardino.

He is documented between 1484 and 1507 in Treviglio, near Milan. His Lombard taste for the decorative effect of rich colours and for plastic modelling was combined with influences of the Paduan and Ferrarese schools. Butinone collaborated closely with his compatriot Bernardo Zenale, a prominent architect and painter. Together they created important altarpieces and frescoes, typical examples of fifteenth century Lombard art.

49 A NATIVITY.
Wood, 46 × 97 cm.
Signed and dated on lower right: 'BUTINONE DA TREVILIUS P. 1493'.

The panel is part of a predella and recalls the style of the altarpiece of the church of San Martino in Treviglio, begun by Butinone and Zenale in 1485.

CABEL, Arent Arentz.

* 1586 in Amsterdam + 1635 in Amsterdam.
He painted winter scenes, huntsmen and fishermen in the manner of Henrik Avercamp. Numerous paintings by the artist are to be found in the museums of Amsterdam, Rotterdam and Antwerp.

50 A FISHERMEN ON A BEACH.
Wood, 26.5 × 52 cm.

CANALETTO, Antonio. (Giovanni Antonio Canal)

* 1697 in Venice + 1768 in Venice.
Antonio, son of Bernardo Canal, a painter of stage scenery, learned his craft in the theatre of Venice. In 1719 he went to Rome and under the influence of Giovanni Paolo Pannini and of the Dutch painter Gaspar van Wittel he started painting scenes and landscapes that were true to life. Back in Venice in 1720 he completed his studies under the guidance of Luca Carlevaris and of the Swedish painter Hans Richter. He became the leading Venetian landscape painter.

53 'IL BUCINTORO'.
Canvas, 57 × 93 cm.

The 'Bucintoro' was the splendid boat used for the spectacular procession which took the Doge to the Lido for the ceremony of the symbolic marriage between Venice and the Sea, during which the Doge threw a ring into the waves. After the return to the Ducal palace, the ceremony turned into a general public festival.
Provenance: Mrs A. L. Snapper Collection, London.

CAPPELLE, Jan van de.

* 1624 or 1625 in Amsterdam + 1697 in Amsterdam.
Although self-taught, Jan van de Cappelle became an outstanding painter of seascapes. The source of his style was the art of Simon de Vlieger. He also painted winter landscapes inspired by Aert van der Neer. His peaceful and harmonious compositions represent seventeenth century Dutch painting at its best.

54 CALM SEA WITH MANY SHIPS.
Canvas, 60 × 68.5 cm.
Signed lower left: 'J. V. Cappelle'.

The smooth surface of the water and the open view between the ships enhance the effect of great calm, typical of the master's mature period. The painting must be dated around 1655-1660.
Provenance: H. E. ten Cate Collection,
De Lutte near Oldenzaal, Holland.

54 A WINTER LANDSCAPE.
Wood, 40.5 × 42 cm.
Signed lower right: 'J. v. Cappelle'.

The painting represents one of the two main subjects of the artist and is a significant example of his skill in rendering a winter atmosphere.
Provenance: H. E. ten Cate Collection,
De Lutte near Oldenzaal, Holland.

CARPACCIO, Vittore.

* around 1455 or 1465 in Venice + 1526 in Venice.
Little is known about his background or his training. Although all the artistic elements of Venetian art of the late fifteenth century are present in his works, Carpaccio remained a solitary artist, guided by his own creative talent, inspired by his notable inventive fantasy and by his refined taste for the decorative element.

56 YOUNG KNIGHT IN A LANDSCAPE.
Canvas, 218.5 × 151.5 cm.
Signed and dated to the right on a label stuck on the tree: 'Victor Carpatius pinxit MDX ...' (the fourth letter is illegible).

The signature and the motto on the left ('MALO MORI QUAM FOEDARI', i.e. better die than defile yourself) appeared only in 1958 after cleaning.

The motto and the white ermine indicate the knight to be a member of the Neapolitan Order of the Ermine. According to the legend, the ermine prefers to die rather than to befoul itself and its white coat symbolizes purity. The Order of the Ermine was founded by Ferdinand I when he decided not to defile himself with the blood of a relative who had taken part in a conspiracy against him. R. Weiss identified the sitter as Francesco Maria della Rovere (1490-1538), heir to the Duchy of Urbino, condottiere of the Venetian army and owner of a palace in Venice. The painting is one of the earliest full-length portraits in European painting and is generally considered one of the artist's masterpieces, belonging to his best period.
Provenance: Otto H. Kahn Collection, New York.

CARRACCI, Ludovico.

* 1555 in Bologna + 1619 in Bologna.
He was the oldest member of a family of artists, known particularly through his cousins Agostino and Annibale, painters active in Ludovico's workshop. Like Caravaggio, he tried in all his paintings to render the natural effect of light, which definitely transformed seicento painting. Guercino, Preti and Crespi were among his most gifted pupils.

56 A PRESENTATION OF THE CHILD IN THE TEMPLE.
Canvas, 122 × 91.5 cm.

This painting emanates the profound religious feeling apparent in all his works. The 'Presentation of the Virgin Mary' is the companion piece to this painting. Both are dated around 1605, and therefore belong to the same period as the frescoes in the Duomo in Piacenza, the high point of Ludovico's artistic life.

CARRIERA, Rosalba.

* 1675 in Venice + 1757 in Venice.
Rosalba Carriera was a born portraitist of noble ladies, making use of gracious and lovely colour tones. Highly appreciated for her particularly soft pearly pastels and for her miniatures, she accomplished an innumerable quantity of commissions at the courts of Paris, Vienna, Denmark and in other European princely houses. Around 1746 loss of sight put an end to her creative activity.

57 PORTRAIT OF A YOUNG LADY AS CERES.
Pastel, 60 × 49 cm.

Provenance: Baron Adolphe de Rothschild Collection, Paris.

CAVALLINI, Pietro. (?)

* around 1250 in Rome + between 1340 and 1350 in Rome.
He worked as fresco painter and mosaicist in the classical Byzantine tradition, in several Neapolitan and Roman churches, such as San Paolo fuori le mura, San Pietro, Santa Maria in Aracoeli. The influence of the young Giotto on the old master is particularly apparent in the frescoes of Santa Cecilia. No panel paintings indisputedly by Cavallini are known.

58 DESCENT FROM THE CROSS.
Poplar, 19.7 × 13.3 cm.

Art critics disagree about the attribution of the panel.
Provenance: Griggs Collection, New York.

CENNI DI FRANCESCO, di Ser Cenni.

Florentine master influenced by Orcagna and Agnolo Gaddi, he was active between 1393 and 1415. He painted a series of frescoes in Volterra and San Gimignano.

59 MADONNA ENTHRONED WITH ANGELS AND APOSTLES.
Poplar, 76 × 50 cm.

Offner identified the subject of this painting as an unusual representation of the 'Pentecost', particularly rare in Florentine painting of the fifteenth century.
Provenance: Kaiser Friedrich Museum, Berlin.

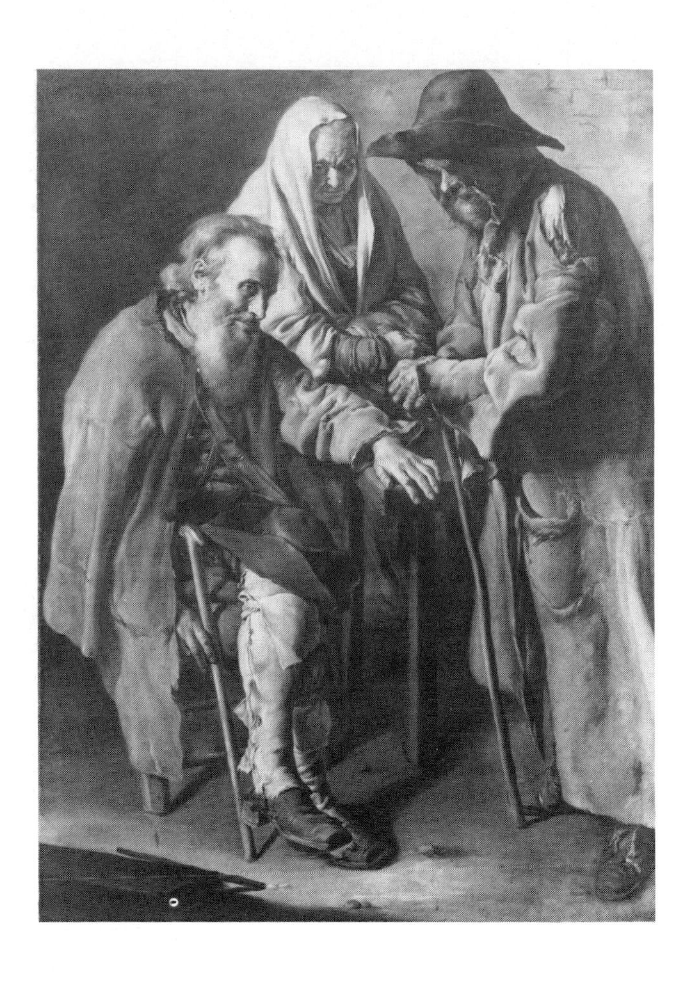

CERUTI, Giacomo called il Pitocchetto.

Active between 1720-1750 in Brescia and probably Venice.
Although the Brescian nobility commissioned their portraits from him and decorated their villas and palaces with his large-size paintings, Ceruti remained ignored by contemporary art critics. Only in this century has he been rediscovered and particularly appreciated for his representations of the poor, beggars, cripples, dwarfs and vagabonds - 'in colours of rags and dust' as described by Roberto Longhi.

59 C THE THREE BEGGARS.
Canvas, 129.5 × 94 cm.

An outstanding example of Ceruti's portraits of the poor and one of his most vigorous and monumental paintings. It is to be listed among the late works of the artist.
Provenance: Vincent Korda Collection, London.

CHARDIN, Jean Baptiste Siméon.

* 1699 in Paris + 1779 in Paris.
He was the son of a carpenter, basically self-taught, although he frequented several workshops. He formed his style copying paintings of Dutch and Flemish artists of the seventeenth century. In 1728 he was admitted to the old Academy of St. Luke and subsequently he became a member of the Academie Royale. He is one of the leading masters of still lifes.

60 STILL LIFE WITH JUG AND COPPER CAULDRON.
Canvas, 32.4 × 39.2 cm.

Plain, rustic kitchen still lifes were frequently painted by Chardin. This was not only because, being of humble bourgeois origins, he was attracted by the simple, but also because there developed in Fance after the splendours of the court of Louis XIV a general preference for the simple Dutch still lifes of the seventeenth century.

CHRISTUS, Petrus.

* around 1410 at Baerle in Brabant + 1472 or 1473 in Bruges.
He was most probably a pupil of Jan van Eyck. After his master's death he took over the workshop in Bruges and completed his unfinished works. Petrus Christus was inspired by Rogier van der Weyden and by the Master of Flémalle. He was the first Dutch portrait artist to place his sitters not against a neutral background as before, but in an interior.

61 OUR LADY OF THE BARREN TREE.
Oak, 14.7 × 12.4 cm.

This unusual representation of the Virgin in a barren tree is due to the fact that Petrus Christus and his wife were members of the Brotherhood of 'Our Lady of the Barren Tree', a community venerating the Immaculate Conception. The small panel was probably a portable altar for the use of one of the brothers of the confraternity, which existed from 1396 and to which clergy and the highest nobility belonged. The Madonna is surrounded by barren branches in the shape of a mandorla. From the branches hang fifteen thin gold chains, each with a small 'a' symbolizing fifteen Hail Marys. To add to the illusion of the letters being of gold, light and shade fall differently on each of them.

CLAUDE LORRAIN (Claude Gellée).

* 1600 at Chamagne near Nancy + 1682 in Rome.
He was probably already in Rome in 1613, and in 1619 he entered the workshop of the landscape painter Agostino Tassi, a pupil of Bril. After a short return home between 1625 and 1627 he settled down in Rome for the rest of his life, painting mainly classical landscapes in the style of Domenichino and of the Carracci. Being a slow and methodical worker, he did not succeed in creating more than a dozen pictures a year even in his most active period, and by the end of his life only two or three. He made a catalogue of 195 drawings after his paintings entitled 'Liber veritatis', which included the dates and the names of his commissioners. Fifty more paintings, however, are to be added to his work.

62 PASTORAL LANDSCAPE WITH THE FLIGHT INTO EGYPT.
Canvas, 193 × 147 cm.
Signed (illegible) and dated: '1663'.

The picture, painted for Duke Lorenzo Colonna, appears in the 'Liber veritatis' as drawing no. 158. According to M. Röthlisberger, it was the first painting Lorrain was commissioned by Lorenzo Colonna. Later he commissioned a further nine paintings and became one of the most important patrons of the artist. This painting is a masterpiece of Claude's late period.
Provenance: Sir David Williams Collection,
Bridehead, Dorset.

CLAESZ, Pieter.

* 1597 or 1598 in Burgsteinfurt + 1661 in Haarlem.
The table prepared for a light meal is the typical subject of the master. From 1617 he resided in Haarlem and he at first based himself on the picture composition of the older local painters of still life. However, he soon reduced the number of objects represented, leaving considerable free space above them, thus obtaining an exceptional depth in his compositions. He left a large number of paintings, many of them often being erroneously attributed to Willem Claesz Heda.

62 A STILL LIFE WITH A BEER-JUG, A PIPE AND PLAYING CARDS.
Wood, 50 × 68 cm.
Signed with the monogram: 'P. C.' and dated on the edge of the table: '1636'.

Provenance: R. H. Smith Collection, Washington.

CLEVE, Joos van.

He is documented from 1511 in Antwerp, where he became a member of the local Guild. It has not been proved whether he came from Antwerp or from Cleve, as has been supposed until now. He probably died in 1541. No signed works by him are known. He may have been active in France as portrait painter at the court of Francis I and the strong Lombard influence in his works suggests a prolonged stay in Milan.

63 SELF-PORTRAIT.
Oak, 38 × 27 cm.

Due to the fact that the artist himself is represented in two 'Adorations of the Magi' in Dresden, this painting can be identified as a self-portrait. The pink in his hand might document it as a wedding portrait, which would date it between 1519 and 1520, as his wedding is known to have taken place in 1519.
Provenance: H. Tietje Collection, Amsterdam.

CLOUET, François.

* around 1505 and 1510 in Tours + 1572 in Paris.
Son of the painter Jean Clouet, called Janet, from whom he inherited not only the nickname but also his position as court painter to King Francis I. Later he was engaged by Henry II, Francis II and Charles IX. Only two signed works by Clouet are known: the portrait of a chemist and the portrait of a lady in the bath, probably representing Marie Touchet, a mistress of Charles IX. Clouet is chiefly known as a painter of portraits and miniatures, but he also painted religious subjects as well as mythological and genre scenes.

64 'LE BILLET DOUX'.
Oak, 41.4 × 55 cm.

Many copies of this painting exist, showing its condition before it was cut at the base. The figures are represented half-length, and the pose of the young woman leaning on the mirror identifies her as a courtesan. The old procuress on the left hands her a letter from her suitor, seen on the right. They evidently represent the well-known 'Trio della Commedia dell'arte' painted by the master to illustrate his moralizing and satyrical ideas: he derides the venal love and naive romantic passion of the gentleman for the courtesan.

COCK, Jan Wellen de.

Recent studies have proved untenable Friedländer's hypothesis that Jan Wellen de Cock, who died in Antwerp shortly before 1527, should be identified with Jan van Leyden. Art historians disagree widely about attributions to the painter.

65 TEMPTATION OF SAINT ANTONY.
Oak, 60 × 45.5 cm.

Ebbinge-Wubben points out the clear Leiden style of the picture which is not consistent with the fact that the painter is documented only in Antwerp.
Provenance: Hans Wendland Collection, Basle.

COLANTONIO (Niccolò Antonio).

Colantonio was active in Naples between 1420 and about 1460. For centuries reports regarding his life and activity were based on errors and misinterpretations. It is known that as a young man at the court of King Réné of Anjou in Naples, he came in contact with Franco-Flemish art and that he was particularly impressed by the paintings of the brothers van Eyck. He was the first Italian painter to use oil, the technique of the great Flemish artists, and was their mediator in Italy. Antonello da Messina was his pupil.

65 A CRUCIFIXION.
Wood, 33 × 44 cm.

The painting clearly reveals the influence of the brothers van Eyck and explains why Colantonio's paintings were until recently attributed either to the brothers van Eyck or to Rogier van der Weyden. At the same time Colantonio anticipates the art of Antonello.
Provenance: Charles R. Henschel Collection, New York.

CORREGGIO (Antonio Allegri).

* around 1489 in Correggio + 1534 in Correggio.
Francesco Bianchi Ferrari is supposed to have been his teacher in Modena, although he was primarily inspired by Costa and Mantegna and in his later works by the great contemporary painters, Leonardo, Raphael and Michelangelo.

68 PORTRAIT OF A SCHOLAR.
Canvas, 55 × 40 cm.

The attribution to Correggio has been accepted by most art historians. During recent cleaning the upper part of the cap and the costume appeared to be later additions.
Provenance: Consul von Weber Collection, Hamburg.

COSSA, Francesco del.

* 1436 in Ferrara + 1478 in Bologna.
Influenced by Cosimo Tura and Mantegna, his style, however, betrays the enduring influence of Piero della Francesca. As his frescoes in the Palazzo Schifanoia in Ferrara were not appreciated, in 1470 he went to Bologna, where he painted his famous altarpieces. He died there of plague while at the peak of his career.

69 SAINT CLARE AND SAINT CATHERINE.
Poplar, each 27 × 8 cm.

Longhi recognized the two panels as parts of the 'Osservanza' altarpiece, now in the Gemäldegalerie in Dresden, painted by Cossa shortly after he had settled in Bologna.
Provenance: Lord Wemyss Collection, Gosford House, Scotland.

70 PORTRAIT OF A MAN HOLDING A RING.
Poplar, 38.3 × 27.3 cm.

The painting was until recently held to be the portrait of the painter Francesco Francia, friend of Cossa, who began working as a goldsmith, as the ring in his hand indicates. Now, however, on account of the elegant costume of the sitter, there is a strong tendency to identify him as a member of the Este family, the ring he is holding being the diamond ring, symbol of that family.
Provenance: von Pannwitz Collection, De Hartekamp, Bennebrock.

COSTA, Lorenzo.

* around 1460 in Ferrara + 1535 in Mantua.
He maintained the tradition of the great Ferrarese painters of the quattrocento, Cosmé Tura and Ercole de' Roberti, assimilating their different styles into one of his own. He was active in Bologna until 1506 when he was called to the court of the Gonzaga in Mantua as successor of Mantegna.

72 GROUP PORTRAIT OF THE BENTIVOGLIO FAMILY.
Canvas, 105 × 82 cm.

The picture represents a family concert held by the Bentivoglio, already portrayed as donors in a fresco in the Bentivoglio chapel in San Giacomo Maggiore, Bologna, in 1488. The painter appears to the left in the foreground with a signature (illegible) and the date '1493' on his cap.
Provenance: Nicholson Collection, London.

73 MADONNA ENTHRONED AGAINST LANDSCAPE.
Poplar, 49.5 × 36.5 cm.

The painting still reveals an influence of Ercole de' Roberti and belongs to the last decade of the fifteenth century, Costa's best period.
Provenance: Heseltine Collection, London.

CRANACH, Hans.

* around 1515 + 1537 in Bologna.
He was the eldest son of Lucas Cranach the Elder, his pupil and member of his workshop. Only two signed works by him are known, both of which are in the Thyssen-Bornemisza Collection.

74 HERCULES AS OMPHALE'S SLAVE.
Beech, 57.7 × 87 cm.
Signed in the centre to the right with the monogram 'HC' (right and left of the winged dragon, the Cranach coat of arms) and dated '1537'.

Over the head of Hercules the quatrain reads: the Lydian girls offer the distaff to Hercules - the god carries out the command of his lady - thus damning lust takes hold of great minds - and gentle love wears down strong hearts. Hercules is represented wearing a woman's cap, sitting at a distaff surrounded by the maids of Omphale, Queen of Lydia. The women evidently enjoy seeing Hercules spinning.

75 PORTRAIT OF A BEARDED MAN.
Wood, 57.5 × 85 cm.
Signed in the centre on the right with the monogram 'HC' and dated '1534'.

The painting is the only known portrait signed by Hans Cranach.
Provenance: Baron von Schenck Collection,
Burg Flechtingen near Magdeburg.

CRANACH, Lucas the Elder.

* 1472 in Kronach + 1553 in Weimar.
His name derives from his birthplace in Franconia where his father, his first teacher, was a painter. After a period of travelling in southern Germany, Lucas settled in Vienna from 1500 to 1504. In 1505 the Elector Frederick the Wise called him to Wittenberg. He was commissioned a great number of altarpieces and devotional pictures but also portraits of princes, reformers and leading citizens. He ran a large workshop with numerous apprentices, including his son.

76 INSIDE AND OUTSIDE SHUTTERS OF AN ALTARPIECE.

Right wing, recto: Saint Anne with the Kneeling Duchess Barbara of Saxony.
Inscribed on the halo: 'Sanct Anna'.

Right wing, verso: Saint George.

Left wing, recto: Saint Elizabeth with the Kneeling Duke George of Saxony.
Inscribed on the halo: 'Sancta Elisaibet'.

Left wing, verso: Saint Christopher.

Each of the four panels, 85 × 30 cm.
The central panel is lost. Painted around 1508.

77 MADONNA AND CHILD WITH A BUNCH OF GRAPES AGAINST A LANDSCAPE.

Wood, 71.3 × 44.3 cm.
Signed on the coping of the wall on the left with the winged dragon.

The bunch of grapes is a symbol of the Passion of Christ. As a favourite theme for devotional pictures, it was represented many times by Cranach in several variants.
Provenance: Henry Schniewind Collection, New York.

78 NYMPH RECLINING BY A SPRING.
Wood, 77.5 × 122 cm.

The reclining Venus, a subject inspired by Giorgione, was represented in several variants in Cranach's workshop. This painting is one of the finest known versions. The precision of the design and the vivid colours are indicative of the beginning of Cranach's late style, around 1525. It is to be dated between 1526 and 1530.
The inscription reads: 'I Nymph of the sacred spring, am resting, don't disturb my sleep'.

80 PORTRAIT OF A YOUNG WOMAN.
Beech, 61 × 42 cm.

Inscribed on the bodice is 'A Bon', which may be interpreted as the beginning of the motto: 'A Bon Fine'. The identification of the sitter as the Duchess Elizabeth of Saxony has been suggested by a miniature in the Dresden book of genealogy. The portrait is datable around 1540 and the attribution to Lucas Cranach the Younger has sometimes been disputed.
Provenance: Prof. Julius Lehmann Collection, Frankfurt.

CUYP, Aelbert.

* 1620 in Dordrecht + 1691 in Dordrecht.
He was pupil of his father Jacob Gerritsz Cuyp, a well-known portrait painter. Aelbert also began as a portraitist, later painting animals and genre scenes as well. After 1645 he turned to landscape painting, influenced by Jan Both, who had returned from Italy where he had assimilated Claude Lorrain's technique of painting landscapes. Cuyp soon established himself as a landscape painter of particular significance due to his sunny, warm evening landscapes with herdsmen and their animals.

82 EVENING LANDSCAPE.
Oak, 47 × 71 cm.

The golden light of the setting sun recalls Claude Lorrain's luminous landscapes. Cuyp owes his success and influence lasting until the eighteenth century to his technique of painting light and to his fluid brush stroke, which so well accorded with the taste of the period.
Provenance: The Hon. Arthur E. Guiness Collection, Holmbury St. Mary, Dorking, Surrey.

DADDI, Bernardo.

* around 1295 in Florence - active until about 1348.
He was one of the first pupils of Giotto, even before Taddeo Gaddi, and he was influenced by the Cecilia-Master and Maso di Banco. Particularly in his late work he approaches the style of the Sienese Ambrogio and Pietro Lorenzetti. The number of his works is so considerable that he must have required the help of numerous assistants.

83 MADONNA AND CHILD.
Poplar, 87.5 × 54.5 cm.

The precision of the modelling of the faces and in particular of the hand holding the Child recall Giotto. The graciousness of the inclination of the head and the harmonious shape of the face indicate, however, the Sienese influence. This is also apparent in the punched halo and in the engraved pattern of the Madonna's robe. The panel has been attributed to the later work of the artist.

83 A CRUCIFIXION.
Gabled panel, 37 × 22 cm.

This panel is the left side of a devotional diptych; the right side, representing a Madonna and Child, is now in an English private collection.

DARET, Jacques.

* between 1403 and 1406 in Tournai, where he is mentioned as companion of Robert Campin, the so-called Master of Flémalle, in whose workshop he remained until 1432. In 1427, together with Rogier van der Weyden, he is documented as apprentice of Campin. Between 1434 and 1452 he worked periodically for the Abbey of St. Vaast at Arras. He is last recorded in 1468 in Bruges. Only four paintings by Daret, revealing a close similarity to the style of Robert Campin, have survived; these are the four outer wings of the St. Vaast altar of 1434. Two of them are now in the Staatliche Museen in Berlin, one is in the Petit Palais in Paris and the fourth is in the Thyssen-Bornemisza Collection.

84 NATIVITY.
Oak, 57 × 52 cm.
The picture depicts a miracle mentioned for the first time in the apocryphal gospel of the pseudo-James and pseudo-Matthew. According to this legend, two midwives were present at the birth of Christ: Zelom believed in the chastity of the Virgin, while Salome demanded tangible proof, with the result that her hand withered, not healing again until she had touched the new-born Child.
Provenance: Pierpont Morgan Library, New York.

DAVID, Gerard.

* around 1460 in Oudewater + 1523 in Bruges.
He was accepted into the Bruges Guild in 1484 as an independent master. He learned his craft, however, in Holland, probably in Haarlem, to judge from the influence of Dieric Bouts and of Geertgen tot Sint Jans noticeable in his early works. Gerard David replaced Hans Memling as leading Bruges master at the end of the fifteenth century, bringing about a renewal of interest in the art of Jan van Eyck.

85 CRUCIFIXION.
Oak, 88 × 56 cm.

This painting can be attributed to his early period because of its closeness to the style of Geertgen tot Sint Jans, and is indirectly based on a lost Crucifixion by the Master of Flémalle. The topography of the city of Jerusalem seen in the background as well as the type of Christ are similar to those of the van Eycks. The male figure to the extreme right, looking at the spectator, might be the painter himself.
Provenance: Convent of the Augustinians,
St. Florian near Linz.

DOLCI, Carlo.

* 1616 in Florence + 1686 in Florence.
He dedicated himself almost exclusively to religious subjects, and with considerable technical ability he executed a great number of small Madonnas and half-length figures of saints in soft and delicate colours. He was also appreciated as a portrait painter.

86 THE YOUNG JESUS WITH A WREATH OF FLOWERS.
Canvas, 103 × 71 cm.
Dated to the left: '1663'.

DOMENICO VENEZIANO.

* around 1410 in Venice + 1461 in Florence.
His artistic development is not known. Various hypotheses relate his formation to Gentile da Fabriano, Jacopo Bellini, Filippo Lippi, Fra Angelico and Uccello. He is documented in Florence in 1439-1445, where together with Piero della Francesca he executed the much admired frescoes in the choir of Sant' Egidio. The few surviving works place Domenico Veneziano among the most important painters of the early Florentine Renaissance.

87 MONK HOLDING CROSS.
Poplar, 69 × 44 cm.

The monk represented is probably St. Philip Benizzi, who died in 1285 as General of the Order of the Servites and is patron saint of Florence. The panel, probably the fragment of a polyptych, is datable between 1445 and 1448.

DOSSI, Dosso and Battista. (Giovanni and Battista Luteri)

Dosso Dossi is considered the leading Ferrarese artist of the first half of the sixteenth century. He died in 1542. His birthdate, as well as that of his brother Battista, is not known, but it is thought to be around 1490. Dosso was probably trained in Venice, where Giorgione and Titian were the leading masters of the time. Around 1514, after several years of activity at the court of the Gonzaga in Mantua, where Lorenzo Costa was the court painter, Dosso entered the service of the Este family in Ferrara. His younger brother Battista collaborated with him. At the court of Ferrara, a cultural centre of the time, Titian and the poet Ariosto became friends of Dosso.

87 A THE STONING OF SAINT STEPHEN.
Canvas, 80 × 90 cm.

Landscapes represent a leading subject in Dosso's paintings, typical being the glimmering of the foliage and the buildings in a shimmering light. The human figures are painted in vivid colours, giving the compositions great vitality.
Provenance: Nottebohm Collection, Hamburg.

DONDUCCI, Giovanni Andrea called Mastelletta.

* 1575 in Bologna + 1655 in Bologna.
His surname derives from his father's profession of tub-maker. The Carracci were his masters and Parmigianino his model. A precocious talent, he surprised everybody with his speed in painting. Although his small landscapes were highly appreciated in Rome, unsatisfied, he soon returned to Bologna where he led a restless life.

87 B REST ON THE FLIGHT INTO EGYPT.
Canvas, 126 × 91 cm.

87 C SAINT JOHN THE BAPTIST PREACHING.
Canvas, 126 × 91 cm.

It is characteristic of Donducci that his small pictures are primarily landscapes, with additional historical or biblical elements. This is also apparent in the two paintings of the Thyssen-Bornemisza Collection, which are considered early works of the artist and are dated 1610.

DOU, Gerrit.

* 1613 in Leiden + 1675 in Leiden.
From 1628 a pupil of Rembrandt, he probably worked with him until the latter left for Amsterdam in 1631-1632. At the beginning, under the influence of his master, he mainly dedicated himself to biblical subjects. Due to his contemplative nature, however, he subsequently gave preference to genre scenes, idyllic and intimate, painted with particular accuracy.

88 GIRL WITH LIGHTED CANDLE AT A WINDOW.
Oak, 26.5 × 19.5 cm.
Rounded top. Signed below window: 'G. Dou'.

The so-called 'niche-scene', a composition of half-lenth figures seen through a window, is characteristic of Dou. The relief under the window sill reappears several times in his compositions. The effect of candle light, more and more frequently represented after 1650, enhances the peaceful atmosphere in his pictures, peacefulness predominant in the interiors later painted by Terborch, de Hooch and Vermeer.
Provenance: Camillo Castiglioni Collection, Vienna.

DUCCIO DI BUONINSEGNA.

* probably around 1255 in Siena + 1319 in Siena.
He was a follower of Cimabue, whose synthesis of Oriental-Byzantine and Western-Gothic elements he adopted with such genius. With his art Duccio became the leader and master of the great period of fourteenth century Sienese painting.

89 B CHRIST AND THE SAMARITAN WOMAN AT THE FOUNTAIN.
Wood, gold base, 43.5 × 46 cm.

In 1308 the Opera del Duomo of Siena commissioned from Duccio a large altarpiece for the high altar. In 1311 Duccio's work was taken from his workshop to the Cathedral in ceremonial procession amid the jubilation of the whole population. Removed in 1506 to make room for a bronze tabernacle, it is now exhibited in the Museo del Duomo in Siena. The panel in the Thyssen-Bornemisza Collection is part of a predella from the back of the altarpiece.
Provenance: Rockefeller jr. Collection, New York.

DÜRER, Albrecht.

* 1471 in Nuremberg + 1528 in Nuremberg.
His father, Albrecht Dürer, a highly regarded goldsmith who had emigrated from Hungary, was his first teacher. In 1486 he became an apprentice in the workshop of Michael Wolgemut (see cat. no. 331) in Nuremberg. In 1490 he started travelling, mainly to meet Martin Schongauer who, however, died in February 1491. He was cordially received by Schongauer's brothers in Colmar and Basle. In 1494 he returned to Nuremberg and married Agnes Frey. The same year he left for Venice and after his return in 1495 he opened his own workshop. He returned to Venice between 1505 and 1507, and in 1520 went to the Netherlands, where he was highly appreciated. His work includes 350 woodcuts, 100 engravings and etchings, over 1000 drawings and about 125 known paintings, besides theoretical studies, his favourite subject during the last years of his life.
'Dürer led Gothic into the style of the Renaissance and created the human prototype of the Reformation; what he accomplished was great enough, but what he overcame may, however, be even greater.' (Wölfflin).

90 JESUS AMONG THE SCRIBES.
Poplar, 67.5 × 80.4 cm.
On the lower left, on a piece of paper hanging from the book, is inscribed the date: '1506' and the monogram 'AD' with the words 'opus quinque dierum' (work of five days).

The inscription indicates that Dürer himself considered the painting, executed in Venice in five days, a piece of bravura. The influence of Leonardo is apparent in the heads of the old men, in contrast with the youthful face of the Christ. The hands of the four scribes, in the centre of the composition, are particularly impressive.
Provenance: Palazzo Barberini, Rome.

DYCK, Anthonis van.

* 1599 in Antwerp + 1641 in London.
At the age of ten he started his apprenticeship in the workshop of Hendrik van Balen and at the age of nineteen was accepted as master by the Guild of Antwerp. Rubens, with whom he collaborated around 1617, praised him as his best pupil. In 1620 van Dyck went to London where he entered the service of King James I. In 1621 he left for Italy, returning in 1627 to Antwerp where he received numerous commissions. In 1632 he went back to London. Although highly honoured wherever he went, he never remained anywhere for a long time, particularly towards the end of his life. In 1634 he stayed in Flanders, in 1640 and 1641 he was in Paris. He died shortly after his return to London.

91 PORTRAIT OF JACQUES LE ROY.
Canvas, 117 × 101 cm.

The portrait was painted in Antwerp in 1631, shortly before he went back to London for the second time. His fluid brush stroke and the confident composition betray Italian, especially Venetian, influence. The sitter held various important offices in Spain and Holland. Van Dyck had painted a portrait of Jacques' son, Philippe Le Roy, in 1630, followed in 1631 by a portrait of the latter's young wife, Marie de Raet.
Provenance: Earl Brownlow Collection, Belton House, Grantham.

EYCK, Jan van.

* around 1390 probably in Maaseyck near Maastricht
\+ 1441 in Bruges.
He was in the service of John of Bavaria in The Hague and later at the court of Philip the Good of Burgundy in Lille. From 1430 he lived in Bruges as the highly regarded town artist. Without any doubt he is one the greatest painters of all time. Although he may not have been the inventor of oil painting, he actually improved the technique to such an extent as to be the first artist to successfully make use of splendid luminous colours.

94 ANNUNCIATION.
Diptych.
Left wing: Angel of the Annunciation.
Right wing: Virgin Annunciate.
Oak, each 39 × 24 cm.

The two figures are painted as being carved in white marble and placed against a background of black marble. The plastic effect is enhanced by the wings of the angel projecting out of the frame and by the shadows of the sculptures on the frames. Usually such grisailles were painted on the outside of altar wings. These two panels, however, have imitation marble painted on the reverse; they may therefore have served as a private devotional diptych. It has been dated around 1436.

FLINCK, Govert.

* 1615 in Cleve + 1660 in Amsterdam.
In 1631-1632 he was a pupil of Rembrandt, as revealed by his early biblical scenes and portraits. From 1640 he developed his own style, with cool colours and a very refined technique, which suited the fashion of the time. He was one of the most appreciated portrait painters of Amsterdam and he received more commissions than any other painter for the decorative history paintings of the town hall. After his death 'The Conspiracy of Claudius Civilis', one of his monumental scenes, was completed by Rembrandt.

95 LANDSCAPE WITH FARMHOUSE AND BRIDGE.
Oak, 36 × 50 cm.

In Flinck's painting, landscapes appear only as background for religious or mythological representations and it is therefore uncertain whether this landscape is to be placed among his works. It shows, however, the strong influence of Rembrandt.

96 PORTRAIT OF A GENTLEMAN.
Oak, 67.5 × 55 cm.
Signed and dated lower right: 'G. Flinck 1640'.

The type of composition and the treatment of light reflect the influence of Rembrandt.

FENZONI, Ferraù called Ferraù da Faenza.

* around 1562 in Faenza + 1645 in Faenza.
A Mannerist of the Roman school around 1600. He was mainly influenced by the style of Andrea Lilio of Ancona, with whom he collaborated on several major works in Rome. In 1599 he returned to Faenza, where as a renowned painter he executed numerous altarpieces and frescoes for the churches of the town and its environs.

95 A SAINT FRANCIS IN ECSTASY.
Canvas, 108 × 82 cm.

FLORENTINE PAINTER CONTEMPORARY OF GIOTTO.

97 CRUCIFIXION.
Poplar, 29 × 20.5 cm.

Suida dated the panel around 1320.

FRAGONARD, Jean-Honoré.

* 1732 in Grasse + 1806 in Paris.
His father, a merchant of Italian origin, was not wealthy and Fragonard was sent to work as an office-boy in a notary's office until he was able to become an apprentice first of Chardin's and later of Boucher's. In 1756 he went to Rome with a scholarship. He returned to Paris in 1761 and in 1765 was accepted by the Académie Royale as painter of historical subjects. On account of his lively temperament, he enjoyed painting highly successful gallant scenes, which were accomplished easily and quickly due to his great virtuosity and exceptional technique. After the Revolution he received only a limited number of commissions and became impoverished.

98 THE SEESAW.
Canvas, 116.8 × 91.4 cm.

This painting is the companion piece to the 'Blind Man's Buff' in the Museum of Toledo, Ohio. Both paintings may be early works, probably executed in Boucher's studio between 1750 and 1752. The great number of old copies shows the popularity of this composition.
Provenance: Maurice de Rothschild Collection,
Château de Pregny, Geneva.

99 PORTRAIT OF MADEMOISELLE DUTHÉ.
Oval canvas (originally round, diameter 53 cm) enlarged to 63 × 53 cm.

This is most probably a portrait of Catherine-Rosalie Gérard, known as Mademoiselle Duthé, the famous actress and mistress of the Count of Artois. Apart from the question of the sitter's identity, Fragonard charms us in this work, as in his large compositions, with his lively technique.
Provenance: John W. Simpson Collection, New York.

FRANCESCO DI GIORGIO MARTINI.

* 1439 in Siena + 1502 in Siena.
He was not only a painter, but also a sculptor, architect, engineer and writer. He shared his workshop with Neroccio dei Landi, who also influenced his style in painting. In 1477 he entered the service of the Duke of Urbino, for whom he created buildings and sculptures over a period of ten years. From 1489 he worked in the Duomo of Siena, first as a sculptor and architect, and from 1498 as master builder of the Duomo. His highly refined and personal style is noticeable in his buildings and sculptures, whereas his painting remained anchored to traditional Sienese schematism.

100 MADONNA AND CHILD WITH SAINT CATHERINE AND ANGELS.
Poplar, 64 × 44 cm.

The panel belongs to the early period of the artist, influenced by Neroccio.

FRANCO-FLEMISH MASTER AROUND 1405-1415.

According to Charles Sterling, he is one of the leading masters at the court of Burgundy, either in Brabant or in Dijon, who with this portrait accomplished one of the outstanding examples of Northern portrait painting.

101 POSTHUMOUS PORTRAIT OF WENCESLAS OF LUXEMBOURG, DUKE OF BRABANT (1337-1383).
Panel transferred to plywood, 34.4 × 25.4 cm.

The name of the sitter is known through an inscription formerly on the back of the panel: 'Wenchcaius dux Brabanciae in antiquitate 34rum annorum'. Wenceslas, younger brother of Charles IV, became the first Duke of Luxembourg in 1354 and in 1355 Duke of Brabant. The style of the painting and the costume suggest a date at the beginning of the fifteenth century, about thirty years after the death of the Duke. The portrait was probably commissioned by Anthony of Burgundy, successor to Wenceslas and one of the sons of Philip the Bold of Burgundy. According to the inventories of 1516, 1524 and 1530 the painting belonged to the collection of Duchess Margaret of Austria, heiress of the Duke of Burgundy.
Provenance: Prince of Liechtenstein Collection,
Schloss Siebenstein.

FRENCH MASTER MID-EIGHTEENTH CENTURY.

102 YOUNG GIRL WITH A DOG.
Canvas, 60 × 49 cm.

This painting was for a long time held to be a portrait by Alexander Roslin of his youngest daughter until Gunnar W. Lundberg excluded it from that painter's work. The picture must therefore be considered the work of an unknown artist. It shows some influence of Boucher and Chardin, but it has its own individual style and reveals the same quality as the child-portraits by Lépicié, Drouais and Colson. The costume indicates a date around 1765.

FYT, Jan.

* 1611 in Antwerp + 1661 in Antwerp.
He resumed the old Flemish tradition of game and table painting passed on to him by his master, Frans Snyders. He enriched his game still lifes with vegetables, fruit, decorative dishes and musical instruments. His rarer flower still lifes, painted with great accuracy and delicacy, are particularly admired.

104 VASE WITH FLOWERS AND ASPARAGUS.
Canvas, 45.5 × 50.7 cm.
Signed lower left: 'Joannes FYT'.

The beautifully arranged flower still lifes, of the painter's late period, are greatly appreciated by collectors.

GAROFALO, Benvenuto Tisi called.

* around 1481 in Ferrara + 1559 in Ferrara.
His teacher was Domenico Panetta, a lesser painter from Ferrara, but he was mainly influenced by Boccaccio Boccaccino and Lorenzo Costa. He was an admirer of Giorgione and was also impressed by Raphael and Michelangelo. Dosso Dossi's inspiration was also of notable importance.

104 A SAINT JEROME AS PENITENT.
Panel, 37 × 41 cm.

The saint, stylistically strongly influenced by Dosso, is represented in front of a landscape which recalls Giorgione. Carlo Volpe dated the panel around 1520 on the basis of a signed picture by Garofalo in the museum of Berlin, dated 1524, representing the same subject.

GADDI, Agnolo.

* around 1350 in Florence + 1396 in Florence.
He was the son of Taddeo Gaddi. After his father's death he took over his workshop and considerably enlarged it. However in his work he followed the archaic tendencies of his father, making no concessions to the taste for International Gothic, at that time also present in Tuscany.

104 C CRUCIFIXION.
Fragment of poplar panel, 34 × 30 cm.

Boskovits dated the panel around 1390-1395, only a few years before the painter's death. The 'Christ on the Cross between the Virgin, St. John and St. Mary Magdalene' was originally the gable of the central panel of a portable altar.

GADDI, Taddeo.

* about 1300 probably in Florence + 1366 in Florence.
Taddeo Gaddi was the best known member of a family of painters with Gaddo Gaddi at its head. Taddeo was a pupil and for many years collaborator of Giotto; he developed, however, his own personal style clearly distinguishable from his teacher's. He has nevertheless been considered the most assured and purest follower of Giotto's artistic principles, and hence as his spiritual heir.

104 D NATIVITY.
Poplar, 34 × 38 cm.

The panel was probably the left wing of a portable altar.
Provenance: Museum of Fine Arts, Boston.

GHIRLANDAIO, Domenico di Tommaso Bigordi.

* 1449 in Florence + 1494 in Florence.
He was a pupil of Baldovinetti and was later influenced by Verrocchio. Together with his younger brothers, David and Benedetto, and a number of assistants, he kept a well-organized workshop. The considerable number of frescoes, altarpieces and pictures testifies to his great activity. 'In his art, creative ability and great inventive variety are combined with a wish to narrate sustained by an uncompromising love of truth and gift of observation, which made him the unequalled chronicler of his time and its society.' (Jan Lauts).

106 PORTRAIT OF GIOVANNA TORNABUONI.
Poplar, 77 × 49 cm.

The inscription on the right reads: 'Could you, art, represent also character and virtue, then no finer painting could exist on earth' and underneath, the date: 1488. Giovanna degli Albizzi married Lorenzo Tornabuoni in 1486. This marriage sealed the reconciliation between two parties who had formerly been adversaries, the aristocratic party of the Albizzi and that of the Medici. The young Giovanna died in childbirth before 1490. The painting is not only one of Ghirlandaio's masterpieces, but also one of the most unforgettable female portraits of Italian painting. The sublime purity of this classical profile impresses us deeply and represents the highest expression of the humanistic culture of the fifteenth century in Florence.
Provenance: J. Pierpont Morgan Library, New York.

GHISLANDI, Giuseppe, Fra Vittore called Fra Galgario.

* 1655 in Bergamo + 1743 in Bergamo.
In 1675 he went to Venice, entering the order of San Francesco di Paola as a lay brother, and in 1702 returned to Bergamo. He painted a considerable number of portraits of important contemporaries and Fra Vittore's great renown as a portrait painter led to clients coming from England, France and Germany to be portrayed by him.

106 A PORTRAIT OF A NOBLEMAN.
Canvas, 93 × 73.5 cm.

The painting is dated around 1735, the late period of the master's activity.

GHIRLANDAIO, Ridolfo.

* 1483 in Florence + 1561 or 1562 in Florence.
After the early death of his father, Domenico Ghirlandaio, Ridolfo was raised and trained as a painter by his two uncles, David and Benedetto. He later perfected his style working with Piero di Cosimo and Francesco Granacci, and this combined with his outstanding talent brought him esteem and success. His style was clearly inspired by his contemporary Florentine masters, especially Leonardo, Fra Bartolomeo and Raphael.

106 C PORTRAIT OF A GENTLEMAN OF THE CAPPONI FAMILY.
Panel, 83 × 61 cm.

In his portraits, Ridolfo Ghirlandaio attained such an outstanding technique that some of them were for a long time considered to be Leonardo's. The picture in the Thyssen-Bornemisza Collection is notable for its excellent psychological interpretation.

GIOVANNI DI PAOLO.

* around 1403 in Siena + 1482 in Siena.
Probably a pupil of Taddeo di Bartolo, he soon developed his own style based on the combined influence of Gentile da Fabriano, Sassetta, of French miniaturists and of Florentine painting.

107 SAINT CATHERINE BEFORE POPE GREGORY XI AT AVIGNON.
Poplar, 28.5 × 28.5 cm.

The panel is part of a polyptych commissioned in 1477 by the Guild of food merchants, the 'Pizzicaioli', to Giovanni di Paolo for the chapel of the hospital of Santa Maria della Scala in Siena. The ten panels of the polyptych represented scenes from the life of St. Catherine. The panel of the Thyssen-Bornemisza Collection shows the saint before Pope Gregory XI at Avignon, where she succeeded in convincing the Pope and the Curia to leave Avignon and return to Rome.
Provenance: Stoclet Collection, Brussels.

108 MADONNA OF HUMILITY WITH ANGELS.
Poplar, gabled, 32.5 × 22.5 cm.

The panel was included by Pope-Hennessy among the late works of the artist, when the former creativeness and vivacity of his art was already reduced.
Provenance: Schniewind Collection, New York.

GOSSAERT, Jan, called Mabuse.

* around 1478 in Maubeuge in Hainault
+ between 1533 and 1536 probably in Middelburg.
He was active in Antwerp as an independent master from 1503 to 1507. Between 1508 and 1509 he was with Philip of Burgundy in Rome. As well as in Antwerp, he was also active in Bruges, Middelburg and Utrecht. On account of the experience gained in Rome and the strong influence of Dürer's art, he became one of the first and most important representatives in the Netherlands of the forms and principles of the Italian Renaissance.

109 ADAM AND EVE.
Panel, rounded top, 56.5 × 37 cm.

The famous engraving of 1504 by Dürer served Gossaert as a model, not, however, to make a copy, but to give it an interpretation of his own.
Provenance: Duke of Anhalt-Dessau Collection,
Gotisches Haus, Wörlitz.

GOYA Y LUCIENTES, Francisco José de.

* 1746 in Fuentetodos near Saragossa + 1828 in Bordeaux.
He grew up in Saragossa and became an apprentice of José Luzan. At the age of seventeen he went to Madrid, where he came in contact with Francisco Bayeu y Subias, Anton Raphael Mengs and Giambattista Tiepolo, painters at the court. From 1769 to 1771 he was in Italy. In 1775 he entered the service of the King of Spain as a designer of the Royal Tapestry Manufactury; later, in 1799, he was appointed court painter to Charles IV. An appreciated portrait painter, he received an exceptional number of commissions too numerous to accomplish. After a stroke in 1792 he lost his hearing; from that time he lived in retirement, inspired by his imagination. In this period he gave birth to his dream-like pictures, the so-called 'Black Paintings'. In 1824 he moved to France and settled in Bordeaux, where, in the last two years of his life, he regained a serenity of spirit which expressed itself in a wide range of colours that led to him being one of the predecessors of the Impressionists.

110 PORTRAIT OF KING FERDINAND VII OF SPAIN.
Canvas, 85 × 63 cm.

Ferdinand VII returned to the throne of Spain after Wellington's victory over the French in March 1814. In September of the same year Goya was commissioned to paint a full-length portrait of the King in coronation robes. The portrait was finished in 1815 and is now in the Oficio del Canal Imperial de Aragon in Saragossa. A second version is in the Prado, Madrid. The half-length portrait of the Thyssen-Bornemisza Collection is probably a preparatory study for the full-length portrait of the King.
Provenance: Don Francisco de Goya de Saenz Collection, Gerona.

111 EL TÍO PAQUETE.
Canvas, 39 × 31 cm.
Inscribed on the back of the canvas before its relining in 1887: 'El celebre ciego fijo', (the famous blind man).

The blind beggar used to sit on the steps of the church of San Felipe el Real in Madrid and was popular as a singer and guitar player. The style of the painting is close to that of the 'Black Paintings' of the early 1820's.
Provenance: Marquis de Heredia Collection.

GOYEN, Jan van.

* 1596 in Leiden + 1656 in The Hague.
Van Goyen was a pupil of Isaack Nicolai Swanenburgh and travelled both to France and in the Netherlands. Jan van Goyen is one of the most typical and important Dutch landscape painters.

112 RECREATION ON THE ICE ON THE MERWEDE AT DORDRECHT.
Canvas, 40 × 61 cm.
Signed and dated to the left, on the lower edge of the strip of land: 'VG 1643'.

Dordrecht is represented in the background, dominated by the Groote Kerk which was rebuilt after a fire in 1457. The tower has a seventeenth century top; the spire was never reconstructed for fear that the tower would sink into the soft soil. It is surprising that van Goyen, as well as the other Dutch landscape painters of the seventeenth century, never painted outside and even this seemingly spontaneous view was painted in his studio.

112 A ON THE BEACH OF SCHEVENINGEN.
Canvas, 91.5 × 107.5 cm.
Signed and dated lower right: 'V. Goyen 1646'.

Behind the dunes dominated by the pointed bell tower of the church of Scheveningen, fishermen are unloading fish from a cart. The picture is distinguished by its calm and serenity, typical of van Goyen's paintings during the last decades of his activity.

GOZZOLI, Benozzo. (Benozzo di Lese di Sandro)

* 1420 in Florence + 1497 in Pistoia.
Benozzo, whose surname Gozzoli appears only in Vasari, is mentioned for the first time in 1444 working in Florence with Ghiberti on the second door of the Baptistery. Before this he was probably a pupil and assistant of Fra Angelico. Between 1459 and 1461 he created his masterpiece, the frescoes in the chapel of the Palazzo Medici in Florence with the particularly suggestive 'Procession of the Holy Kings'. His twenty-five frescoes with biblical scenes in the Camposanto at Pisa were almost entirely destroyed by bombing during the Second World War. Less impressive than Gozzoli's frescoes are his panel paintings illustrating the way of life, customs and historical figures of Renaissance Florence and the beauty of the Tuscan landscape.

113 SAINT JEROME WITH A MONK.
Poplar, 29.7 × 50.8 cm.

The panel is part of a predella and has a companion piece representing two female saints in the museum at Béziers. The central panel, now missing, probably represented a Pietà.

EL GRECO. (Domenikos Theotokopoulos)

* 1541 in Crete + 1614 in Toledo.
Already as a child in his own country he had learned from monks how to paint icons. In his early years he went to Venice and became a pupil of Titian. His study of the leading contemporary Venetian masters, particularly Tintoretto, Veronese and Bassano, is clearly traceable in his work. After staying in Parma and in Rome, he moved to Spain in 1577 and settled in Toledo. His hope of being involved in the decoration of the Escorial was not fulfilled as Philip II did not appreciate the altarpiece representing the 'Martyrdom of Saint Maurice' he had commissioned from El Greco. In 1586 he painted his famous 'Burial of the Count of Orgaz', which led to a considerable number of important commissions for altarpieces in churches and convents in Toledo and its environs.

114 LAST SUPPER.
Canvas, 121 × 190 cm.

This picture, clearly Venetian in style, shows the influence of Tintoretto in particular. It is considered an early work, painted while El Greco was still in Venice.

114 A ANNUNCIATION.
Canvas, 117 × 98 cm.

This painting belongs to his Italian, probably to his Roman, period and differs from the Annunciation (cat. no. 118), a work of his maturity. As a composition it resembles the Annunciation painted by Titian for the church of San Salvatore in Venice. Strong influences of Veronese and Tintoretto are evident, and the painting represents a happy synthesis of El Greco's heritage from the great Venetian masters.
Provenance: Contini Bonacossi Collection, Florence.

115 MATER DOLOROSA.
Canvas, 63 × 48 cm.

El Greco painted many versions of the same subject. This typical example of his highly expressive smaller head studies of saints, was dated by Mayer around 1585.
Provenance: Dr Felix Schlayer Collection, Madrid.

116 CHRIST WITH THE CROSS.
Canvas, 66 × 52.5 cm.
Signed in Greek letters to the right on the foot of the cross: 'domenikos theotokopoulos epóiei'.

According to Mayer, the painting is the precursor of several representations of the 'Man of Sorrows' by El Greco, the best example of which is now in the Prado. Dated around 1602-1607.
Provenance: G. Neumans Collection, Paris.

117 THE IMMACULATE CONCEPTION.
Canvas, 108 × 82 cm.

The composition was interpreted as the 'Assumption' until Mayer recognized it as the 'Immaculate Conception' in 1911. One of the favourite subjects in Spanish painting of the sixteenth and seventeenth centuries, it was also frequently represented by El Greco. The landscape was probably painted by the son of El Greco, Jorge Manuel.
Provenance: Marczell von Nemes Collection, Budapest.

118 ANNUNCIATION.
Canvas, 114 × 67 cm.

Twenty-five paintings of the Annunciation by El Greco are known. The Annunciation in the Thyssen-Bornemisza Collection is supposed to be a preparatory study for the central panel of the triptych painted by El Greco in 1660 for the Colegio de Doña Maria de Aragon in Madrid.
Provenance: Pascual Collection, Barcelona.

GUARDI, Francesco.

* 1712 in Venice + 1793 in Venice.
Francesco learned his craft in the workshop of his elder brother Giovanni Antonio and became his collaborator. Townscapes were his favourite subject, based on the vedute painting of Canaletto, who may have been his teacher. In contrast to Canaletto's precise and realistic representation of perspective, Francesco Guardi in his vedute strives to express the quality of the atmosphere with his fluid and vibrating brush-stroke.

119 CANAL GRANDE WITH SANTA LUCIA AND SANTA MARIA OF NAZARETH.

120 CANAL GRANDE WITH SAN SIMEONE PICCOLO AND SANTA LUCIA.

Canvases, each 48 × 78 cm.

The two paintings are companion pieces and illustrate both sides of the Canal Grande. The church of Santa Lucia was demolished in the middle of the last century to make way for the building of Venice railway station. Zampetti dated the two paintings around 1780, as late works of the master.

Provenance: Leonard Gow Collection, Camis Eskan, Cragendoran, Dumbartonshire.

GUERCINO (Giovan Francesco Barbieri).

* 1591 at Cento near Ferrara + 1666 in Bologna.
Guercino spent the first fifty years of his life in his native town of Cento, except for long periods in Bologna, Venice, Rome and Piacenza. In 1642 he settled in Bologna and after the death of Guido Reni he became the leading master of the Bolognese school of painters. His work may be divided into three periods: an early period influenced by Caravaggio, a middle period dedicated to the 'sfumato' and his maturity influenced by the late style of Guido Reni.

122 A CHRIST AND THE SAMARITAN WOMAN AT THE WELL.
Canvas, 116 × 156 cm.

Of the three versions of this subject, painted by Guercino in 1640, 1641 and 1648, according to Prof. Volpe this must be considered as one of the two earlier ones. The influence of Guido Reni is evident.

HALS, Frans.

* between 1581 and 1585 in Antwerp + 1666 in Haarlem.
His parents settled in Haarlem in 1590. Between 1600 and 1603 Frans Hals became an apprentice of the painter and writer Karel van Mander. From a wealth of almost exhuberant colours apparent in his early works, the master gradually chose a darker tonality. He is particularly important for Dutch portrait painting, which he enlivened with fresh realism, on account of his unrestrained style and individuality.

123 FISHERMAN PLAYING THE VIOLIN.
Canvas, 83.5 × 67.5 cm.

The style of the painting dates it around 1630. The landscape in the background was probably painted by Pieter Molyn (1595-1661). Although the fisherman reveals a spontaneous joy of life, he may well also have had an allegorical significance for a seventeenth century observer.
Provenance: Ant. Reyre Collection, Ireland.

124 FAMILY GROUP WITH NEGRO SERVANT, IN A LANDSCAPE.
Canvas, 202 × 285 cm.

The family represented has not yet been identified. The negro servant might indicate that the head of the family made his fortune in the West Indies. Following an old Dutch tradition, Frans Hals used symbols in order to enhance the meaning of his painting; in this picture the way the couple are holding hands and the dog symbolize true fidelity. The personality of each member of the family is brought out sharply. The landscape in the background has been attributed to Pieter Molyn. The painting was executed around 1645.
Provenance: The Mogmar Art Foundation, New York.

HAMEN Y LEÓN, Juan van der.

* 1596 in Madrid + 1631 in Madrid.
He was the son of an officer of the King's guard who had come to Spain from Brussels. The father, who also painted, was the first and probably the only teacher of his son, who became highly significant in Spanish still-life painting of the seventeenth century. His works have often been mistaken for paintings by Zurbarán.

125 STILL LIFE.
Canvas, 77 × 100 cm.

For a long time this still life was attributed to Francisco de Zurbarán until Sterling, comparing it with a signed and dated still life in the National Gallery in Washington, firmly identified it as a work by Hamen Y León.
Provenance: Dr von Frey Collection, Paris.

HEDA, Willem Claesz.

* 1593 probably in Haarlem + between 1680 and 1682 in Haarlem.
He created a new type of Dutch still life in Haarlem: the 'Monochrome Banquet', a composition in shaded colours with a limited number of objects, laying stress on the diagonal, the whole being unified by his use of light.

126 STILL LIFE.
Oak, 43.5 × 68 cm.
Signed and dated on the blade of the knife: 'HEDA 1634 f'.

This still life shows some of the frequently recurring objects in Heda's work: the large rummer, the broken glass, the overturned silver 'tazza', the pewter plate with a partly peeled lemon and the pewter dish with pastry.

HEEM, Jan Davidsz de.

* 1606 in Utrecht + 1683 in Antwerp.
He learned his craft in Utrecht from Balthasar van der Ast, and later in Haarlem he became familiar with the still lifes of Pieter Claesz and Willem Claesz Heda, an influence apparent in his early works. From about 1626 until 1635 he resided in Leiden, where his painting betrays his indecision regarding choice of subject. In 1636 he settled in Antwerp, and under the influence of Daniel Seghers attained a mature and personal style. His still lifes are rich and splendid.

128 STILL LIFE.
Oak, 54.5 × 41 cm.
Signed upper right: 'J D De Heem'.

This composition reveals great skill: the accent, which is slightly to the left, is created by the reflection of the carafe and by the bent ears of wheat. In the seventeenth century flower still lifes were related to the concept of transience, whereas the ears symbolized resurrection and eternal life.

HEEMSKERCK, Maerten van.

* 1498 in Heemskerck near Haarlem + 1574 in Haarlem.
After being a pupil of Cornelius Willemsz in Haarlem and of Jan Lucasz in Delft, in 1527 he entered the workshop of Jan van Scorel in Haarlem, copying his style to such an extent that their works could no longer be distinguished. In 1529 Heemskerck opened his own workshop and painted a series of portraits still close to van Scorel but already testifying to his matured artistic personality. In 1532 he went to Rome and his return to Haarlem is only documented in 1538. While in Italy his style changed noticeably under the influence of Michelangelo and Giulio Romano.

129 PORTRAIT OF A LADY WITH SPINDLE AND DISTAFF.
Panel, 104 × 84.5 cm.

Although the portrait has been attributed to the early period of Jan van Scorel, it clearly reveals the characteristic elements of Heemskerck's early style. It is dated around 1529, before he went to Italy. The sitter and the coat of arms on the wall have not yet been identified. The spindle and the distaff symbolize the virtues of the mistress of the house. 'Undoubtedly this portrait represents one of Heemskerck's greatest achievements as a portrait painter and is one of the finest portraits of Dutch sixteenth century art.' (Ebbinge-Wubben).
Provenance: Earl of Caledon Collection, Kinard,
County Tyrone, Eire.

HELST, Bartholomäeus van der.

* probably 1613 in Haarlem + 1670 in Amsterdam.
He was probably a pupil of Nicolaes Elias in Amsterdam, as might be seen from a certain lack of fluidness in his early works. His 1639 picture of 'The Riflemen', now in the Rijksmuseum, shows, however, a notable progression and an essential change of style which cannot be explained without the study of the group portraits of Frans Hals. Besides his group portraits, van der Helst also produced a series of family and single portraits that are among the best examples of the decorative style in Dutch portrait painting.

130 PORTRAIT OF A NOTARY OR MERCHANT.
Canvas, 105 × 88 cm.

Painted around 1650 when he was at the height of his powers. The colour scheme is pleasant, the execution precise and the interpretation appropriate.

HEYDEN, Jan van der.

* 1637 in Gorkum + 1712 in Amsterdam.
He painted mainly townscapes and landscapes with architectural elements. In contrast to the traditional painting of vedute, however, he was less interested in topographical faithfulness than in the elegance of the composition.

131 FOREST LANDSCAPE WITH CROSSROADS.
Oak, 44.5 × 55 cm.
Signed lower right: 'VHeyden'.

According to Hofstede de Groot the staffage with the small figures was painted by Adriaen van de Velde.
Provenance: Lady Theodora Guest Collection, London.

131 A TOWN FORTIFICATION.
Wood, 29 × 34.7 cm.
Signed lower right: 'J. V. Heyden'.

The detailed execution and the fine quality of the colouring are typical of the style of the master.
Provenance: H. E. ten Cate Collection,
De Lutte near Oldenzaal.

HOBBEMA, Meindert.

* 1638 in Amsterdam + 1709 in Amsterdam.
Around 1657 Hobbema must have been a pupil of Jacob van Ruisdael, whose influence is noticeable in his work. Hobbema's art is bright, clever in its construction, graceful in its detailing, with radiant colours and lighting.

132 TREES ON WATER.
Canvas, 70 × 90 cm.
Signed lower left: 'm. hobbema'.

In composition and details the picture is based on Jacob van Ruisdael's engraving 'The Travellers' and is datable shortly before 1660. In contrast to the sombre atmosphere of Ruisdael's engraving, this landscape is cheerful in accordance with the gay and decorative style of Hobbema's art, a style that anticipates the eighteenth century.
Provenance: Prince Liechtenstein Collection, Vienna.

HOLBEIN, Hans the Elder.

* around 1465 probably in Augsburg, where he is documented as son of the tanner Michael Holbein. It is not known where he received his artistic education. In 1493 he is citizen of Ulm, in 1494 his name appears for the first time in the tax book of Augsburg, where the date of his death, 1524, is also found. Altarpieces, portraits, silver point and pen drawings represent the work of Hans Holbein the Elder, to be placed between Late Gothic and Renaissance. His attempts to represent the individuality of the figures prepared the ground for the art of his son, Hans Holbein the Younger, the great portrait painter.

134 PORTRAIT OF A MAN.

135 PORTRAIT OF A WOMAN.
Both vellum, on copper beech, 23.7 × 17.2 cm.

As appears from an old inscription on the back, in the seventeenth century the two paintings were mistakenly considered to be portraits of Martin Luther and his wife Catherine Bora. In 1923 Suida attributed them to Hans Holbein the Elder. The technique and the style indicate that they were painted at the same time and were probably companion pieces, since they also correspond in size. It is hard to know whether the sitters were husband and wife, father and daughter or bride and bridegroom.
Provenance: Count Attems Collection, Graz.

HOLBEIN, Hans the Younger.

* probably 1497 in Augsburg + 1543 in London.
He learned his craft, together with his elder brother Ambrosius, in the workshop of his father, Hans Holbein the Elder, in Augsburg. After travelling in 1513-1514, from 1515 he worked as an apprentice in Basle and in 1519 became a master in the painters' Guild. In 1526 he left for England, settling in London. After 1536 he worked permanently in the service of King Henry VIII until his death in London from plague. He was a close friend of Erasmus of Rotterdam and Thomas More. He was influenced mainly by Leonardo, Bramante, Dürer and Baldung-Grien. As a painter and illustrator, Hans Holbein the Younger is to be considered one of the greatest artists of all time. 'His art is a synthesis of the most rigorous realism and of a feeling for beauty of form.' (P. Ganz).

136 A PORTRAIT OF THOMAS CROMWELL.
Wood, tondo, diameter 10.2 cm.

Thomas Cromwell was an important personage at the court of Henry VIII. Son of a farrier from Putney, in 1531 he became royal counsellor, in 1532 the King's treasurer, in 1534 secretary to Henry VIII, in 1539 Lord Chancellor and Earl of Essex. He was, however, beheaded in 1540 as a supporter of Henry's marriage to Anne of Cleves and of Protestant politics. Holbein painted three different portraits of Cromwell, which points to their close relationship. Paul Ganz supposes Cromwell to have been one of Holbein's first patrons in London and the one who introduced him at court. The tondo was painted around 1532-1534.
Provenance: Jacques Seligman Collection, New York.

136 PORTRAIT OF KING HENRY VIII OF ENGLAND.
Oak, 28 × 20 cm.

The portrait appears 'to have been a sample in which Holbein gave excellent proof of his ability in order to obtain the patronage of Henry VIII' (P. Ganz). It was probably painted around 1537, shortly after the King's marriage to Jane Seymour. Of the surviving portraits of the King by Holbein, this is the only one entirely executed by him.
Provenance: Earl Spencer Collection, Althorp, England.

HOOCH, Pieter de.

* 1629 in Rotterdam + after 1684 probably in Amsterdam.
He was a pupil of the landscape painter Nicolas Berchem in Haarlem. In 1655 he was inscribed in the painters' Guild in Delft, where he remained until 1660. Here he gave preference to his principal subjects, representing interiors, quiet streets and courtyards. It was his best creative period. Later he settled in Amsterdam, where, however, the precision of his interiors appears reduced and his vivid and warm colours become dark and sombre, his conception of space weaker and his style merely decorative.

138 LADY WITH NEEDLEWORK AND CHILD IN A ROOM.
Canvas, 55 × 45 cm.

The picture represents a Dutch 'Vorhuis', the room which one entered directly through the front door. The seat of the sewing lady is protected by wooden planks against the cold floor, a piece of gold leather is hanging behind the chair. Heavily overpainted probably in the nineteenth century, the painting regained its original colour after restoration in 1958. It was executed shortly after de Hooch settled in Amsterdam, around 1662-1663.
Provenance: Institute of Arts, Minneapolis.

139 INTERIOR OF THE COUNCIL CHAMBER IN THE TOWN HALL IN AMSTERDAM, WITH VISITORS.
Canvas, 112.5 × 99 cm.
Signed lower left: 'P. D Hooch'.

The former town hall of Amsterdam is now the Royal Palace. A view of the exterior of the building is represented in painting cat. no. 30 by Berckheyde, 'Flower market in Amsterdam'. The painting is one of the finest works by de Hooch from his Amsterdam period, and also has great importance as an historical document illustrating the original condition of the hall, which was inaugurated in 1655. It conveys the impression of warmth and calm distinction offered to the visitor in the seventeenth century.
Provenance: W. J. R. Dreesmann Collection, Amsterdam.

HUBER, Wolf.

* around 1485 in Feldkirch, Vorarlberg + 1553 in Passau.
Together with Altdorfer and Lucas Cranach the Elder, Huber was the leading master of the 'Donauschule'. He is believed to have settled in Passau in 1510, where he was employed until his death as painter and architect to the local bishops. In 1541 he is documented as town-builder. Of his works only about 30 paintings, a dozen woodcuts and several highly appreciated drawings have survived. His most important work is the altarpiece of St. Anne, executed for his native town between 1515 and 1521 and today divided in many parts.

140 PORTRAIT OF AN ELDERLY FEMALE MEMBER OF THE REUSS FAMILY.
Pine, 43 × 32.7 cm.
On the back: the coat of arms of the Reuss family and the hardly legible date, probably 1534.

The seven portraits by Wolf Huber still preserved, including the one in the Thyssen-Bornemisza Collection, testify to an intensity of expression and a subtle rendering of the personality of the sitter.
Provenance: Count Attems Collection, Graz.

141 ADORATION OF THE MAGI IN THE SNOW.
Lime, 63 × 44.8 cm.

The attribution of this painting to Wolf Huber is due to Baldass, who also points out an affinity with the work of Altdorfer. Winziger excludes it from the work of Huber, attributing the picture to a painter called by him 'Master of the Lugano Adoration', a pupil of Wolf Huber.
Provenance: J. Reder Collection, Brussels.

INGANNATI, Pietro degli.

He is first documented in 1524 in Venice, where in 1530 he was inscribed as a member of the painters' Guild. As a follower of Giovanni Bellini, he sometimes used Bellini's compositions for his own paintings. Later he was influenced by Palma Vecchio.

142 MADONNA AND CHILD WITH SAINT AGNES IN A LANDSCAPE.
Poplar, 60.5 × 85.5 cm.

The same figure of St. Agnes appears repeatedly in the works of Ingannati, and corresponds exactly to the 'Young Woman as Saint Agnes', a signed work in the Art Museum of Portland, Oregon.

ISENBRANT, Adriaen.

From 1510 documentable in Bruges + 1551 in Bruges.
Isenbrant was a highly regarded member of the painters' Guild in Bruges. Together with Gerard David, he kept up the tradition of Bruges painting derived from Jan van Eyck, Rogier van der Weyden and Hans Memling, which after his death lost its significance.

144 REST ON THE FLIGHT INTO EGYPT.
Oak, 43.5 × 29.5 cm.

In the background the Massacre of the Innocents in Bethlehem. The Madonna type closely resembles that of Gerard David. A similar representation of the same subject by Isenbrant is in the Alte Pinakothek in Munich. Here the background, as in all of Isenbrant's paintings, is rendered with the utmost care.
Provenance: Joseph Crawhall Collection, London.

JORDAENS, Jacob.

* 1593 in Antwerp + 1678 in Antwerp.
He was a pupil of Rubens' teacher, Adam van Noort. Jordaens was mainly influenced by van Dyck and Rubens, his famous contemporaries, and after their deaths for almost forty years he was the leading Flemish painter. The quality of his allegorical and mythological scenes and his closeness to the feelings and way of life of common people prevented him from being only an imitator of these two great masters. He received numerous commissions also from abroad, remaining active until old age, although his late works lack form and vivid colours.

145 HOLY FAMILY WITH ANGEL.
Canvas, 102 × 91.5 cm.

The painting must have been executed shortly after 1618 and reveals the influence of Caravaggio in the modelling of the figures and in the contrast of chiaroscuro. Two variants of this composition are known, one in Kassel and the other in San Francisco.

146 PORTRAIT OF A GENTLEMAN AT THE AGE OF 73.
Canvas, 147 × 116 cm.
Dated lower left: 'AETATIS 73 A° 1641'

This is a companion piece to the portrait of a seated elderly lady, today in the museum in Brussels. The sitters have not been identified.
Provenance: Edmond Huybrechts Collection, Antwerp.

JUAN de Flandes.

* ? in Flanders + 1519 in Palencia, Castile.
He was a painter from Flanders, probably from Bruges, who in 1498 was appointed court painter by Queen Isabella of Castile. After Isabella's death in 1504 he was active in Palencia. His most important work is a series of small panels representing scenes from the life of Christ and the Virgin, which originally formed part of the 'Oratorium' painted for Isabella. Dürer admired the 'Oratorium' in Mechlin in 1521.

147 PORTRAIT OF A SPANISH PRINCESS.
Oak, 31.5 × 22 cm.

According to recent studies, the sitter is presumed to be one of the daughters of Queen Isabella. It might be either Johanna, married to Philip the Handsome in 1496, who after the latter's premature death became known in history as Joanna the Mad; or her younger sister Catherine of Aragon, first wife of Henry VIII and mother of Mary Tudor. The portrait was painted around 1496.
Provenance: Duke of Infantado Collection, Madrid.

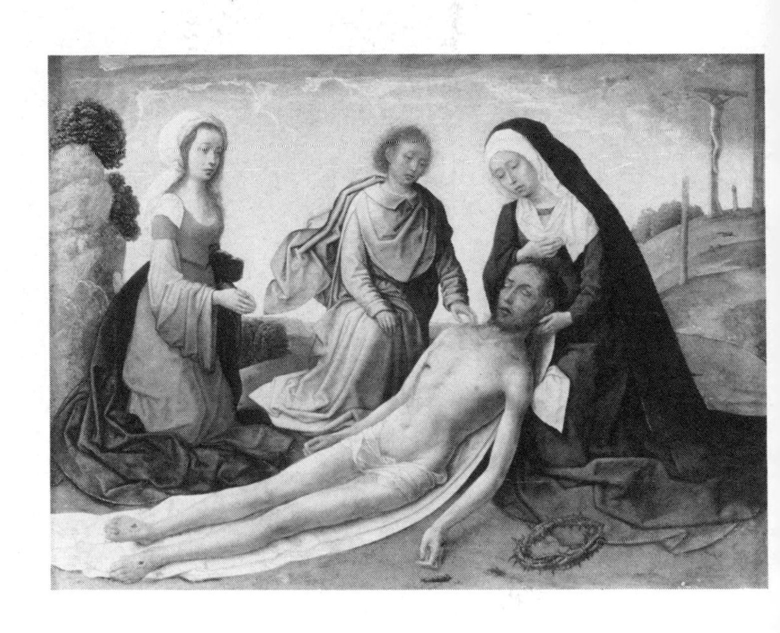

148 PIETÀ WITH SAINT JOHN AND SAINT MARY MAGDALEN.
Oak, 23 × 30 cm.

The panel was attributed by Friedländer to Hugo van der Goes. The face of Christ and the type of composition are very close to the 'Lamentation' by Hugo van der Goes in the museum of Vienna. On the other hand, the soft colours, the facial types and the modelling of the other two figures are characteristic of Juan de Flandes, to whom it is to be attributed.
Provenance: Duke of Blacas Collection, France.

KALF, Willem.

* 1619 in Rotterdam + 1693 in Amsterdam.
He was probably a pupil of Frans Ryckhals in Dordrecht. From 1638 until the end of 1646 he was active in Paris, painting small-size cottage and kitchen interiors and still lifes with vessels in precious metal. From 1654 until his death he lived in Amsterdam, attaining a perfect pictorial technique in his late works. Willem Kalf is considered the most important Dutch painter of still lifes.

149 STILL LIFE.
Canvas, 64 × 55 cm.
Signed and dated upper left: 'W. Kalf 1660'.

The objects represented here frequently reappear, even identically arranged, in Kalf's still lifes from his Amsterdam period. At that time lemons and oranges symbolized wealth. The open watch, an allusion to the passing of time, is reminiscent of the 'Vanitas' still life.

150 STILL LIFE WITH NAUTILUS CUP.
Canvas, 79 × 67 cm.
Signed upper left: 'Willem Kalf Fecit'.
Dated upper right: 'Anno 1660'.

The painting is one of the finest examples of Kalf's still lifes. He used to represent precious Chinese bowls, silver salvers, porcelain dishes, Venetian glasses together with fruit and oriental carpets, with particular precision and taste.
Provenance: H. E. ten Cate Collection,
De Lutte near Oldenzaal, Holland.

151 KETEL, Cornelis.

* 1548 in Gouda, near Rotterdam + 1616 in Amsterdam.
At the age of eleven he became a pupil of his uncle, a glass painter, who had the same name. In 1565 he entered the workshop of Anthonis Blocklandt in Delft. After a long period spent in France, he went to England in 1573, where he painted portraits of German merchants and, later, of members of the court. In 1578 he portrayed Queen Elizabeth I. From 1581 until his death he lived in Amsterdam. Only portraits by Ketel have been preserved, although he was also a painter of allegorical and Biblical scenes and was active as a sculptor, poet and architect. He gave new inspiration to portrait painting in Amsterdam.

PORTRAIT OF A GENTLEMAN AT THE AGE OF 58.
Oak, 82 × 67 cm.
Signed upper left: 'AN° 1594 AET. 58'.

152 PORTRAIT OF A LADY AT THE AGE OF 56.
Oak, 82 × 67 cm.
Signed upper left: ‘AN° 1594 AET. 56’.

The two panels probably represent husband and wife. The way in which the half-length figures fill the space of the painting is characteristic of Ketel’s work in this period. Faces and hands stand out forcefully from the dark draperies. De Keyser and Frans Hals continued this kind of portraiture in the seventeenth century.
Provenance: Mrs Mesdag - van Calcar Collection, The Hague.

KEY. Adriaen Thomasz.

* around 1544 probably in Antwerp
+ probably 1589 in Antwerp.
Only a few documents exist regarding Key's life. In 1558 he became an apprentice in the workshop of Jan Hack and in 1568 an independent master in the painters' Guild of Antwerp. Primarily a portrait painter, he was highly appreciated. A sober and precise style is characteristic of his portraits.

153 PORTRAIT OF PRINCE WILLIAM I OF ORANGE (1533-1584).
Oak, 45 × 33 cm.
Dated upper left: '1579'.

Of the many existing versions of this portrait, which differ to varying degrees, the three best examples, considered to be by Key's own hand, are in the Rijksmuseum in Amsterdam, in the Mauritshuis in The Hague and in the Thyssen-Bornemisza Collection.

KEYSER, Thomas de.

* 1596 or 1597 in Amsterdam + 1667 in Amsterdam.
The activity of de Keyser as a portrait painter in Amsterdam was almost contemporary with that of Frans Hals in Haarlem. The art of portrait painting in Amsterdam had, however, a particularly lifelike quality, which explains why de Keyser's portraits are essentially more reserved in conception than those of Frans Hals. De Keyser is considered the most important portrait painter in Amsterdam before Rembrandt.

154 FAMILY PORTRAIT, A MOTHER WITH DAUGHTER AND SON.
Oak, 70 × 50 cm.
Signed on the right armrest: 'TDK' and dated '1632'.

De Keyser was one of the first portrait painters to introduce small full-length portraits in an interior. The mother is holding a watch at which the boy is pointing, an allusion to the passing of time and to the transience of generations.

KOERBECKE, Johann.

* around 1410-1420 in Münster, Westphalia + 1491 in Münster. The influence of the Master of Schöppingen, of Conrad von Soest and of Stefan Lochner determined his art. The high altar completed in 1457 for the Cistercian convent of Marienfeld (Münster) is his major work. The panel in the Thyssen-Bornemisza Collection formed the lower right corner of the inside of the right wing.

155 ASSUMPTION OF THE VIRGIN.
Oak, 93 × 65 cm.

A central carved shrine flanked by two painted wings, each 210 cm. high and 150 cm. wide, formed the altarpiece. Four scenes from Christ's Passion are represented on the outside of the two outer wings, while on the inside of each there are four scenes from the Life of the Virgin on a gold background. Probably in 1804, after the closure of the convent, the wings were split up and sawed into pieces, being sold separately during the following decades. With the exception of one panel, all the sixteen scenes can be traced to museums and collections in Europe and the United States.

KONINCK, Philips.

* 1619 in Amsterdam + 1688 in Amsterdam.
Koninck was the son of a wealthy goldsmith. In 1637 he was apprenticed to his brother Jacob in Rotterdam. In 1641 he settled in Amsterdam, and as the owner of a shipping service to Rotterdam he was very wealthy. Belonging to Rembrandt's circle of friends he was strongly influenced by the master in his early work. Around 1654 he developed a style of his own, painting wide, panoramic landscapes and views over open plains which are unique in Dutch art.

156 DISTANT VIEW IN GELDERLAND.
Canvas, 84 × 127 cm.
Signed and dated on the house in the left foreground:
'p. koninck 1655'.

In this landscape Philips Koninck has already brought his 'panorama-style' to perfection. From a hillside in the foreground one's vision is led over flat land towards the far distance. Parallel lines of trees, rivers and villages, emphasized by the chiaroscuro of the clouds, create the depth of the painting. This landscape continues the style of Seghers and Van Goyen, but Koninck replaces their warm tonality with a lighter colour-scheme.
Provenance: James Simon Collection, Berlin.

KULMBACH, Hans Süss von.

* around 1480 probably in Kulmbach near Bayreuth
+ 1522 in Nuremberg.
Kulmbach is mentioned in contemporary documents as an apprentice of Jacopo de' Barbari and Albrecht Dürer. The influence of Jacopo de' Barbari as well as the close relationship with Dürer are apparent in Kulmbach's paintings. Apart from painting altarpieces and portraits, he was also a designer of woodcuts and stained-glass windows.

157 THE ROSARY TRIPTYCH.
Central panel: in a garland of five groups of ten roses are represented the Trinity, the Madonna, Angels, Patriarchs, Prophets, Apostles, Martyrs, Confessors and Virgins; below, Purgatory.
The painting represents the graces obtained through the rosary.
Pine, 117.2 × 84.3 cm.

Left wing, inside: Presentation of the Virgin in the Temple. Outside split off and lost.
Pine, 123 × 38.5 cm.

Right wing, inside: Meeting of Joachim and Anne at the Golden Gate. Outside split off and lost.
Pine, 123 × 38.8 cm.

Comparing this work with a woodcut of the 'Rosary' by Kulmbach, dated 1515, F. Winkler proposes the same date for the altarpiece.
Provenance: Prince of Thurn and Taxis Collection, Regensburg.

LANCRET, Nicolas.

* 1690 in Paris + 1743 in Paris.
After being trained by Pierre Dulin, the painter of historical subjects, in 1712 he was active in the workshop of Claude Gillot together with Watteau, whose influence was so strong that the paintings Lancret sent to the 'Exposition de la jeunesse' were mistaken for Watteau's. Later Lancret specialized in representing 'fêtes galantes', and had great success due to careful execution and clever staging of the figures.

161 THE SWING (L'ESCARPOLETTE).
Canvas, 64 × 51 cm.

The painting resembles a scene on a stage with the actors placed by an expert director. The triangle of trees creates the required depth; the stage is closed at the back by a pergola and a fountain.
Provenance: Roger Pettiward Collection,
Finborough Hall, Suffolk.

161 A THE EARTH.
Canvas, 38 × 31 cm.

The painting is part of a series of five, representing the four elements: air, water (two scenes), earth and fire. They were ordered by the Marquis de Bèringhen, the first equerry of King Louis XV.
Provenance: Countess Carnavon Collection.

LE NAIN, Antoine.

* around 1588 in Laon + 1648 in Paris.
He was the eldest of three brothers who from 1629 had a workshop together in Paris. Antoine was a specialist in portraits, Louis (1593-1648) painted rural scenes, Mathieu (1607-1637) historical and religious subjects. Their works, generally created in collaboration, are only signed 'Le Nain', which makes it difficult to identify the individual hands. Antoine, who was head of the workshop, became master of the Guild of St. Luke in 1629; in 1648 all three became members of the newly founded Académie Royale.

162 CHILDREN SINGING AND FIDDLING.
Oak, 19.5 × 25.5 cm.

The painting is datable shortly after 1640. The careful modelling of the heads and the grouping of the figures correspond to the style of Antoine, while the folds of the clothes painted with a fluid brush-stroke and the modelling of the bodies are closer to Louis.
Provenance: Lord Swansea Collection, Singleton.

LEYDEN, Aert Claesz, called Aertgen van.

* 1498 in Leiden + 1564 in Leiden.
In 1516 he became a pupil of Cornelis Engebrechtsz. His work reveals the influence of various artists: Lucas van Leyden, Jan van Scorel, Maerten van Heemskerck, and the South German painters of the 'Donauschule' also determined his style.

164 PORTRAIT OF A MAN.
Oak, 25 × 22 cm.
Signed upper right with monogram 'L' and dated '1511'.

The portrait was previously attributed to Lucas van Leyden. It must belong to a period when Aertgen was mainly influenced by Lucas, shortly after 1530.
Provenance: M. M. van Valkenburg Collection, The Hague.

LEYDEN, Lucas Hugensz van.

* 1494 in Leiden + 1533 in Leiden.
Lucas van Leyden, an infant prodigy, was already executing etchings and watercolours at the age of 12-14, probably instructed by his father. After 1508 he entered the workshop of Cornelis Engebrechtsz. Around 1521 in Antwerp he met Dürer, who had a decisive influence on his artistic development.

164 A CARD PLAYERS.
Canvas, 29.8 × 39.5 cm.

Friedländer already considered the severity of the lady and of the two gentlemen unsuitable for a game of cards. Hence a symbolic or moral interpretation should be sought. The game of cards might symbolize an amorous relationship, in which case it would indicate the rivalry between the two gentlemen for the favour of the lady. An interesting hypothesis was put forward by A. Rosenbaum: if one tries to identify the sitters by comparing their likenesses with those in other portraits, the younger of the card players betrays a similarity to Charles V, and the card player on the right might be Henry VIII's ambassador, Cardinal Wolsey. The lady might be identified as the Regent of the Netherlands, Margaret of Austria, and the game of cards would thus have a political significance. The year 1521, the date of the meeting of these historical personalities in Bruges, when the painter on his way to meet Albrecht Dürer was also present, is confirmed by stylistic analysis.
Provenance: Lady Dunsany Collection, Dunsany Castle.

164 D SAINT PAUL.
Wood, 44 × 21 cm.
Signed and dated on the stone on the lower left: 'H 1515'.

The painting testifies to the strong influence of Dürer on the early work of Lucas van Leyden. The initial 'H' is uncommon for the master, and according to R. Winkler refers to his second name (that of his father) Hugensz. It is probably a fragment of an altarpiece.
Provenance: Prof. Wilhelm Suida Collection, New York.

LUCA DI TOMMÈ.

* around 1330 + after 1389.
Luca di Tommè was one of the leading masters of the Sienese school in the late trecento and a highly appreciated painter of his time. He was influenced by Pietro Lorenzetti, Simone Martini and Lippo Memmi.

164 B ADORATION OF THE MAGI.
Poplar, 41 × 42 cm.

Together with a Crucifixion now in the De Young Memorial Museum of San Francisco, this panel is part of the predella of an altarpiece. Stylistically the painting belongs to the mature period of the master, to be dated around 1366.
Provenance: Robert von Hirsch Collection, Basle.

LORENZO VENEZIANO.

Documented between 1356 and 1372 in Venice.
Lorenzo was a pupil and collaborator of Paolo Veneziano. Elongated Gothic forms, fine detailing, splendour and swing of the gowns, brilliant graduating colours, a tendency to a decorative effect and a taste for goldsmith's art, are the characteristics of his style. While working in Bologna around 1368, he was impressed by miniature painting.

164 C PORTABLE TRIPTICH.
Poplar, central panel 83 × 30 cm., laterals each 83 × 15 cm.

Central panel: Crucifixion; in predella: SS Lucy, Nicholas, Helen and Margaret; in the finial: St. Veronica.

Left wing: Archangel Gabriel; Trinity; St. Anne with Madonna and Child; St. Francis receiving stigmata; female figure in the finial; St. Christopher on the back.

Right wing: The Virgin Annunciate; Baptism of Christ; Conversion of St. Paul; SS Anthony of Padua, Anthony Abbot, Louis of Anjou; male figure in the finial; St. James the Great on the back.
Provenance: Humphrey Brooke Collection, London.

LIEVENS, Jan.

* 1607 in Leiden + 1674 in Amsterdam.
Lievens was pupil of Joris Verschooten in Leiden and of Pieter Lastman in Amsterdam. He worked with Rembrandt, both artists stimulating each other. After his stay in England (1632-1634), where he was deeply impressed by the painting of Van Dyck, he settled in Antwerp. In 1644 he returned to Amsterdam. The works of Lievens were more highly appreciated by contemporaries than the paintings of Rembrandt.

166 LANDSCAPE WITH REST ON THE FLIGHT.
Oak, 35 × 52 cm.

The style of the landscape is close to Rembrandt. The quality of his colour scheme suggests a date toward the end of his stay in Antwerp, where he was particularly impressed by the landscapes of Brouwer, or a date shortly after he settled in Amsterdam, i.e. after 1644. Clouds, trees and hills are dominating elements in comparison to the small figures.
Provenance: T. Cottrell Dormer Collection, London.

LONGHI, Pietro Falca called.

* 1702 in Venice + 1785 in Venice.
Longhi studied painting with Antonio Balestra in Venice and with Giuseppe Crespi in Bologna. Soon, however, his bizarre and capricious talent led him to develop his own style. In his paintings he illustrates with humour and irony Venetian life of the eighteenth century. Longhi's work was popular in expression, remaining however gentle and sober. His pictures were highly appreciated and commanded substantial prices.

167 A THE GAME OF TICKLING.
Canvas, 61 × 48 cm.

The scene takes place in a noble Venetian palace of the eighteenth century. The young girls amuse themselves teasing a young man in an armchair, tickling him. The three Graces observe the joyful scene from a picture on the wall.

LOO, Jakob van.

* around 1614 in Sluys, Netherlands + 1670 in Paris.
Jakob was pupil of his father, Jan van Loo, and from 1642 to 1660 lived in Amsterdam as a successful painter. In 1660 he fled to Paris to avoid prosecution for manslaughter and made a name for himself as a portrait painter of renown.

168 GROUP OF MUSICIANS.
Canvas, 73 × 65.5 cm.
Signed bottom of the table: 'I. v Loo'.

A replica of the painting, of about the same size, was acquired by Catherine II of Russia and is now in the Hermitage in Leningrad. Both paintings must have been executed in Amsterdam around 1650.
Provenance: S. Bugge Collection, Copenhagen.

LOTTO, Lorenzo.

* around 1480 in Venice + 1556 in Loreto.
Almost forgotten in the last century, the importance of Lotto as one of the leading painters of the first half of the sixteenth century has been recognized by modern art critics, particularly Berenson. Nothing is known about his artistic education. Antonello da Messina, Giovanni Bellini and Dürer influenced his style. Already in his early works he detached himself from the warm colour scheme and classical, balanced compositions typical of Venetian painting from the time of Bellini and Giorgione. His compositions are animated and restless, his colour scheme cold, as if reflecting the unsettled life of the artist.

168 A BETROTHAL OF THE VIRGIN.
Poplar, 45 × 35 cm.

According to Pallucchini, the picture is an important early work of the painter, to be dated around 1508. It represents an event from the apocryphal Gospel, referring to the divine choice of Joseph as the betrothed of the Virgin; he is kneeling in the temple in front of the priest, presenting the lily with a bird resting on it, symbol of the 'verga fiorita'. The rejected suitor is breaking his staff as a sign of his resignation.

168 B SELF-PORTRAIT.
Poplar, 43 × 35 cm.

Zeri attributed the portrait to Lorenzo Lotto, identifying it as a self-portrait on account of the position of the sitter and the angle of his look, corresponding to the position of the painter who is looking at himself in a mirror while painting his own portrait.

LUINI, Bernardino.

* around 1486 probably in Milan + 1532.
His date of birth and details regarding his life, education, artistic relations and travels are unknown. Luini was undoubtedly the most important painter of his generation in Lombardy. One of his major works is the Crucifixion in the church of Santa Maria degli Angeli in Lugano. In his paintings the influence of Leonardo is apparent, particularly in his late period. He was also inspired by Foppa, Borgognone, Solario, Bramantino and Raphael.

168 C MADONNA AND CHILD WITH INFANT SAINT JOHN.
Canvas, 86 × 60 cm.

The painting belongs to the middle period of Luini, around 1523-1525, and reveals the dominant influence of Leonardo.
Provenance: Edouard de Rothschild Collection, Paris.

MAES, Nicolaes.

* 1634 in Dordrecht + 1693 in Amsterdam.
Around 1648 Maes was active in Rembrandt's workshop in Amsterdam, after having probably been the pupil of a painter in Dordrecht. In 1653 he returned to his native town and began to represent scenes from everyday life in the house, in the children's room and the kitchen, in the style of Rembrandt. Subsequently he dedicated himself more and more to portrait painting, exclusively from 1660. In 1673 he settled in Amsterdam. An active and successful painter, he was an important representative of Baroque painting in Holland.

169 THE NAUGHTY DRUMMER.
Canvas, 62 × 66 cm.

The self-portrait of the painter appears in the mirror on the wall, hence the painting may represent a portrait of the artist's family. Thus the young mother would be Adriana Brouwers, widow of the minister Arnoldus de Gelder, who married Maes in 1654. The young drummer, who is waking up his sister Johanna, is Adriana's son by her first marriage. The picture is one of the artist's best genre paintings, from the period shortly after 1654.
Provenance: Prince of Sachsen-Meiningen Collection.

170 PORTRAIT OF A GENTLEMAN.
Canvas, 90 × 70 cm.
Signed below centre: 'Maes'.

171 PORTRAIT OF A LADY.
Canvas, 90 × 70 cm.
Signed and dated lower right: 'N. Maes. 1667'.

The two portraits are companion pieces, probably representing the secretary of the Amsterdam Town Council Harmen van de Poll and his wife Brechtje von Hooft. The Lady is wearing a lace collar and cuffs of a rare and precious Flemish lace, the so-called 'Point de Dieppe'.
Provenance: Prince of Wied Collection, Neuwied.

MAESTRO PAOLO VENEZIANO.

Documented between 1333 and 1358.
Paolo Veneziano was the most important artist at the birth of Venetian painting. Although still clearly rooted in Byzantine art, he was also closely connected with the Gothic movement and particularly with Giotto's art; his painting thus represents a synthesis of both styles. His masterpiece, the famous 'Pala feriale' of 1345, a retable for the 'Pala d'Oro' in San Marco, shows a technical refinement unequalled by any other painter of his period, testifying to the high level of Venetian culture in the fourteenth century.

173 MADONNA OF HUMILITY WITH ANGELS, AND DONOR PRESENTED BY DEATH.
Poplar, rounded top, 68 × 57 cm.

Comparing it with other dated paintings of the master, the panel is datable around 1355.

MAFFEI, Francesco.

* around 1620 in Vicenza + 1660 in Padua.
Painter of the Venetian school and brilliant decorator, several of whose ceilings are still preserved in Venetian churches. He was influenced by Tintoretto, Fetti, Liss and Strozzi.

173 A SAINT MICHAEL OVERTHROWING LUCIFER.
Stone, 80 × 75 cm.

MALER, Hans.

*around 1490 in Ulm + around 1530.
On the back of the portrait of Anton Fugger, painted in 1524, Maler signed: 'Hans Maler von Ulm Maler zuo Schwatz'. This proves that he was born in Ulm and was active as a painter in Schwaz near Innsbruck, where he executed several portraits for the Fugger trading family and for the court of Ferdinand I in Innsbruck. His early paintings point to his being a pupil of Bartolomäus Zeitblom, a master from Ulm; he was later influenced by Dürer.

174 PORTRAIT OF QUEEN ANNE OF HUNGARY AND BOHEMIA (1503-1547).
Wood, 44 × 33.5 cm.

Hans Maler painted several portraits of the Queen, wife of Ferdinand I. On the basis of a dated woodcut used as a model, the portrait is datable before 1519.
Provenance: Palazzo Barberini, Rome.

175 CRUCIFIXION.

176 CHRIST IN LIMBO.
Both on wood, each 89 × 37.5 cm.

Both are inside panels of the wings of an altarpiece. The scenes represented are based on the model of Dürer's engravings of the Passion. On the back of the second panel is the date 1520 or 1521.

MANCADAN, Jacobus Sibrandi.

Probably born in Groningen between 1634 and 1639, he is documented as mayor in Franecker and in 1645 as citizen of Leeuwarden. At first he dedicated himself to landscape painting mainly with figures of peasants, and later to allegorical and mythological subjects.

184 A LANDSCAPE WITH FIGURES.
Wood, 30.5 × 41 cm.

MARATTA, Carlo.

* 1625 in Camerano, Marches + 1713 in Rome.
Maratta, pupil of Andrea Sacchi, was influenced by Pietro da Cortona and by Lanfranco. Although a good portraitist, he dedicated himself mainly to religious subjects. He was among the most appreciated decorators of Roman churches of his time and for decades influenced Roman religious painting.

184 B SAINT MARK.
Canvas, 101 × 74.5 cm.

The painting is one of the representations of the four Evangelists painted by Maratta around 1670 for Cardinal Antonio Barberini.

MAGNASCO, Alessandro.

* 1667 in Genoa + 1749 in Genoa.
After the untimely death of his father Stefano, whose pupil he had been, Alessandro Magnasco went to Milan, where he was active in the workshop of the Venetian Filippo Abbiati. From early on he was a successful portrait painter, although none of his portraits have come down to us. He soon turned to scenes with small figures, which became his speciality. In 1735 he returned to Genoa, where, however, he did not attain the success he had achieved in Milan.

184 C WOOD LANDSCAPE WITH MONKS AND OTHER FIGURES.
Canvas, 233 × 173 cm.

Landscapes with monks represent his favourite subject. The style of these paintings, always with small figures, is unusual and is marked by fluent and rapid brushstrokes which only outline the slim proportions of his figures. This shows that Magnasco, despite his strong individuality, was faithful to the tradition of his time, bridging Late Baroque and Rococo.

MARIESCHI, Michele.

* 1710 in Venice + 1744 in Venice.
Probably a pupil of Gaspare Diziani, he later entered the workshop of Canaletto. The earliest documentation refers to a journey to Germany and his activity there as stage decorator at the Saxon court. Returning to Venice in 1736, he became a member of the painters' Guild. As both painter and engraver he gave preference to views of Venice, revealing the strong influence of Canaletto.

186 A VIEW OF THE CANAL GRANDE
WITH SANTA MARIA DELLA SALUTE.
Canvas, 85 × 127 cm.

Marieschi repeated the view of Santa Maria della Salute in different versions, one of which is in the Louvre.
Provenance: Dimitri Tziracopoulo Collection, Athens.

MASTER OF THE ANDRÉ MADONNA.

An anonymous painter active in Bruges towards the end of the fifteenth century. The name derives from a half-length Madonna in a landscape in the Musée Jacquemart-André in Paris. 'A true descendent and heir of Jan van Eyck, who connects in form and way of painting the virtues of the heroic period with the milder taste of his generation'. (M. J. Friedländer).

189 MADONNA SURROUNDED BY FOUR ANGELS, STANDING IN AN ARCH.
Oak, 62 × 32 cm.

In the background is Bruges, recognizable by the high tower of the church of Our Lady. 'This picture, miniature-like, delicately executed and with the gracefulness of the fifteenth century preserved, appears as a late flower of the art of Van Eyck'. (M. J. Friedländer).
Provenance: Edouard Simon Collection, Berlin.

MASTER BERTRAM.

* around 1340 probably in Minden, Westphalia
+ 1414 in Hamburg.
Although little is known of Master Bertram's artistic training, certain characteristics of his style indicate his connection with Bohemian masters. From 1367 he is documented in Hamburg. In his principal work, the Grabow altarpiece in the Kunsthalle Hamburg, he appears as a leading master of High Gothic painting in Northern Germany.

191 TRIPTYCH: 'SANCTA FACIES CHRISTI' WITH ANGELS PLAYING INSTRUMENTS.

Central panel: 'Sancta Facies Christi'.
Oak, 30.8 × 24.1 cm.

Left wing: Angel playing the fiddle; on verso: the Archangel Gabriel. Inscribed on the scroll: 'Ave Maria gra[t]ia plena dominus te'.

Right wing: Angel playing the harp; on verso: the Virgin Annunciate.
Both wings, oak, each 30.8 × 12 cm.

The representations of the 'Sancta Facies Christi', particularly popular in the Middle Ages, derive from the sudarium of Veronica preserved in St. Peter's, Rome. Prayers before this 'Sancta Facies' would grant indulgencies. This small altarpiece was certainly intended for private devotional use. Datable between 1395 and 1410.

MASTER FROM COLOGNE, around 1450-1460.

The origin of the painter of the panel has not yet been established. On account of certain affinities to the 'Master of the Darmstadt Passion', Stange attributed the painting to the 'Master of the Vision of St. John' active in Cologne between 1450 and 1460, who learned his craft in the workshop of the 'Master of the Darmstadt Passion' on the middle Rhine.

193 SAINTS COSMAS, DAMIAN AND PANTALEON.
Oak, 131.5 × 72 cm.

Saints Cosmas and Damian, twins and doctors, were beheaded during Diocletian's persecutions. St. Pantaleon, also a doctor, was martyred under the Emperor Maximilian. The saints are the patrons of the sick and of doctors. The panel was probably the inside of a side-wing of an altarpiece with as its counterpart the 'Adoration of the Magi', now in the Museum of Art in Toledo, USA.
Provenance: Wallraf-Richartz-Museum, Cologne.

MASTER OF FLÉMALLE. (Robert Campin)

* before 1380 in Tournai + 1444 in Tournai.
This anonymous master, not much older than Rogier van der Weyden and van Eyck, is one of the founders of Dutch panel painting. His name derives from a Triptych in the Städelschen Kunstinstitut in Frankfurt, which is believed to have come from a convent in Flémalle near Liège. The close relationship with the work of Rogier van der Weyden and Jacques Daret suggests the painter is one and the same as Robert Campin, the documented teacher of both painters.

194 PORTRAIT OF ROBERT DE MASMINES.
Oak, 35 × 24 cm.
Still in the original profile frame.

Two slightly different versions of this portrait are known, the second one in the Kaiser Friedrich Museum in Berlin. On account of a portrait drawing in the Recueil d'Arras, the sitter has been identified as Robert de Masmines, counsellor and commanding officer to the Dukes of Burgundy, who died during the siege of Bouvignes in 1430.
Provenance: Count van de Straten-Ponthoz Collection,
Château de Ponthoz, Ocquier near Huy, Belgium.

MASTER OF FRANKFURT.

* around 1460
+ probably in the first quarter of the sixteenth century.
He was probably a painter from Antwerp, owing his name to two paintings in Frankfurt: the St. Anne altar and the Crucifixion altar of the Humbracht family. Several biblical representations and some portraits can be attributed to the same master. He probably belonged to the circle of Jan Joest von Kalkar and chose Joos van Cleve and Hugo van der Goes as his models.

195 HOLY FAMILY.
Oak, 77 × 58 cm.

Typical of the master is his accuracy in rendering the thickly grown vegetation forming a screen before the landscape. Many of the plants represented are Marian symbols of beneficence.

MASTER OF GROSSGMAIN.

Active in Salzburg and Passau, he owes his name to an altarpiece in the parish church of Grossgmain near Salzburg, dated 1499. Together with Frueauf, he was one of the leading masters in Salzburg towards the end of the fifteenth century.

196 SAINT JEROME.
Pine, 66.5 × 49 cm.
Dated on the left page of the open book: '1498'.

St. Jerome is wearing cardinal's robes, stroking the lion from whose paw, according to the tradition of the Legenda Aurea, he had removed a thorn. The open book indicates his Latin translation of the Bible. Simplicity of forms and accentuation of the volume of the bodies are indicative of the master. Restricting himself to the essential, he strives to bring out the dignity and statuesque quality of his figures.
Provenance: A. Figdor Collection, Vienna.

MASTER OF THE INTERNATIONAL GOTHIC STYLE,
around 1410.

The period of Gothic painting between the last decades of the fourteenth century and about 1450 is called 'International Gothic'. The preference for brilliant colours and design are indicative of the painting of this period. From the general insecurity of this time probably arose the longing for a paradise which could at least be realized in painting.

197 VOTIVE PAINTING WITH THE TWO SAINT JOHNS AND DONOR.
Oak, 191 × 121 cm.

The heraldist H. Bird has convincingly identified the donor as Henry V of England, and the dating of the panel around 1410 is also confirmed by heraldic research. Therefore the painter of the picture will probably have been an English master of the International Gothic style, although for a long time the work was attributed to an early Spanish master.
Provenance: Dr Gustav Schneeli Collection,
Château de Vuippens, Switzerland.

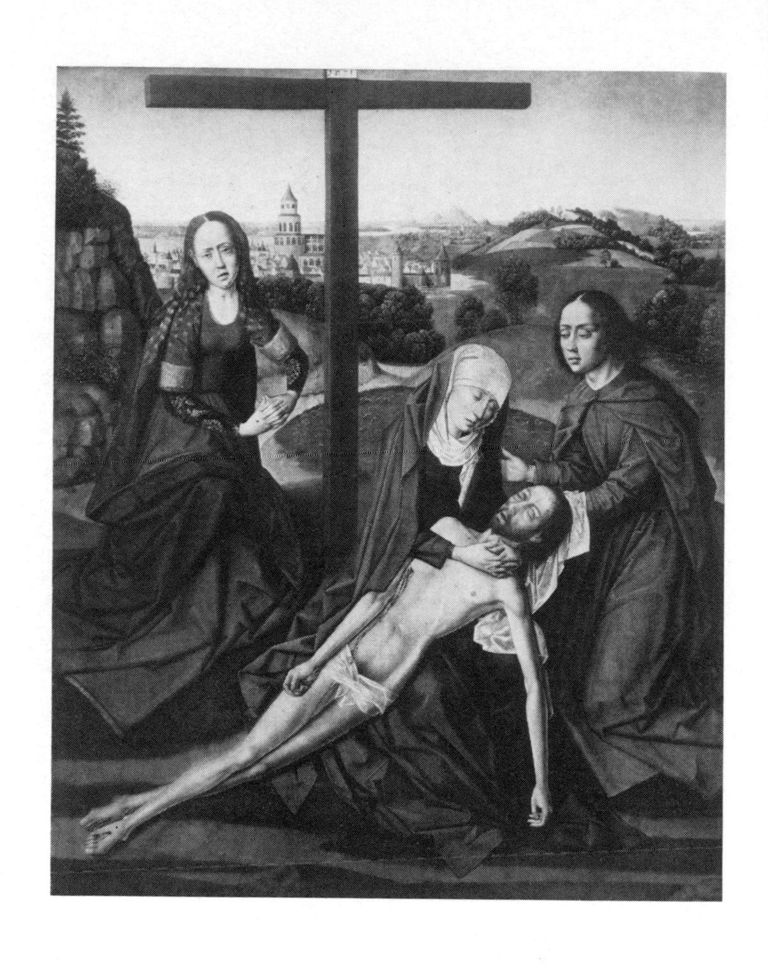

MASTER OF THE LEGEND OF SAINT LUCY.

Named after the altarpiece depicting the legend of St. Lucy in the church of St. James in Bruges. Probably active in Bruges in the last quarter of the fifteenth century, he formed his style on the line of Memling and Rogier van der Weyden. Spanish elements noticeable in his works suggest the master's presence for a time in Spain.

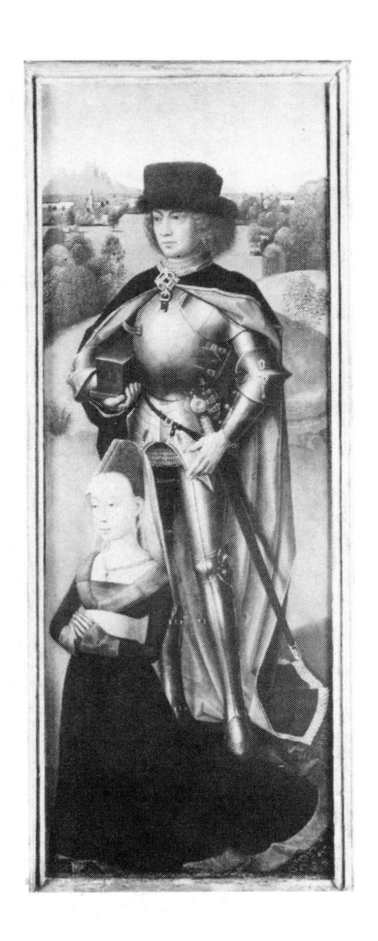

198 TRIPTYCH WITH THE LAMENTATION OVER CHRIST.
Oak, central panel 75 × 61 cm.,
laterals each 75 × 27 cm.

With the exception of the figure of Mary Magdalen to the left, the central panel represents a slightly different version of the Lamentation by Dieric Bouts in the Louvre. On the left wing is represented the donor with St. Donatian, on the right wing the female donor with St. Adrian. St. Peter and St. Barbara in grisaille appear on the outer sides of the wings.
Provenance: Joseph Spiridon Collection, Paris.

MASTER FROM LÜBECK, around 1480-1490.

It has not yet been possible to identify this artist, close to the circle of Bernt Notke. The affinity in style between the panel and painting in Lübeck around 1480-1490, particularly the woodcuts of the Lübeck Bible of 1494, is so apparent that earlier attributions are no longer valid.

199 PORTRAIT OF A YOUNG MAN.
Lime, 62 × 39 cm.
Still in the original frame.

The young man has not yet been identified. Perhaps the statue of Samson, on a bracket, might be an indication of the sitter.
Provenance: Lüneburg Museum.

MASTER OF THE LYVERSBERG PASSION.

Active in Cologne in the third quarter of the fifteenth century, he owes his name to a cycle of the Passion once in the Lyversberg Collection and now in the Wallraf-Richartz Museum in Cologne.

200 DEPOSITION, ENTOMBMENT, DESCENT INTO LIMBO, RESURRECTION.
Oak, 164 × 55.8 cm.

This panel is probably the right wing, and the only surviving fragment, of an altarpiece originally in the Franciscan church of St. Magdalen of Bethania at Düren, completed in 1470. The Crucifixion was probably depicted in the central panel. The representation of St. Louis of Toulouse on the verso of the right wing was split off and is lost.
Provenance: Prince Hohenzollern-Sigmaringen Collection.

MASTER OF THE MAGDALEN ALTARPIECE.

Florentine painter active in the second half of the thirteenth century, he owes his name to a panel depicting St. Mary Magdalen in the Galleria dell'Accademia in Florence.

201 MADONNA ENTHRONED WITH TWO SAINTS AND ANGELS.
Wood, gabled, 177 × 87 cm.

Coor Achenbach, comparing the painting with the panel 'St. Mary Magdalen and Scenes from her Life' in the Accademia of Florence, attributed the Thyssen panel to the master and considered it to be 'one of the finest examples of thirteenth century Florentine painting'. She identified the two saints from the fragmentary inscriptions as Dominic and Maximus of Aix, who also appear in the painting in the Accademia in Florence. The Thyssen panel was executed between 1270 and 1275.

MASTER OF SAINTE GUDULE.

The master owes his name to a panel 'The Preaching of a Saint' in the Louvre, with the façade of the church of St. Gudule in Brussels in the background. The painter was a Dutch master active in Brussels between 1470 and 1490.

204 CLOTHING OF THE NAKED.
Oak, 63.5 × 41.5 cm.

The panel belongs to a group of representations of the seven works of charity. Only one other panel of the same series, the 'Liberation of the Prisoners', is preserved in the Cluny Museum in Paris. On account of the costumes, the painting is datable between 1466 and 1472.
Provenance: Albert Figdor Collection, Vienna.

MASTER FROM ULM, around 1470-1480.

205 PORTRAIT OF A WOMAN.
Pine, 50.5 × 39.3 cm.

Provenance: Private Collection, Berlin.

206 PORTRAIT OF A MAN.
Pine, 55 × 43.5 cm.

Provenance: Marczell von Nemes Collection, Munich.

The female portrait, cut on top and on both sides, no longer corresponds to the size of the companion piece. Friedländer attributed the portrait to a 'South German Master of 1480'. Buchner proposed a 'Swabian Master, probably from Ulm, between 1470 and 1480'.

MASTER FROM ULM, around 1510.

207 TWO WINGS FROM AN ALTARPIECE OF THE PREMONSTRATENSIAN CONVENT OF MARCHTAL.

Left wing: outside, St. Anne with the Virgin and the Christ Child with Abbot Simon Götz as donor.
Inside: Adoration of the Shepherds.
Pine, 160 × 65.5 cm.

Right wing: outside, St. Elizabeth distributing bread and wine to two beggars.
Inside: Presentation of Christ in the Temple.
Pine, 160.2 × 65.5 cm.
Both panels in original frame.

The representations on the inside of the panels are partly based on engravings by Martin Schongauer and Albrecht Dürer. The central panel as well as the predella with the four Church Fathers, is lost. Abbot Simon Götz remained in office until 1514, which dates the panels around 1510.
Provenance: Fürstlich-Liechtensteinische Gemälde-Galerie, Vienna.

MASTER OF THE URSULA LEGEND.

The anonymous master active in Bruges around 1480-1490 owes his name to two altar wings each with four scenes from the legend of St. Ursula, today in the Groeninge Museum in Bruges. The painter was influenced by Rogier van der Weyden and by Memling.

208 MADONNA AND CHILD WITH TWO ANGELS.
Oak, 36 × 26 cm.

This composition was repeatedly depicted, with variations, in the workshop of this master.
Provenance: Prince Hohenzollern-Sigmaringen Collection, Schloss Sigmaringen.

MASTER FROM VENICE, around 1300.

Longhi identified this master as Cimabue, Toesca believed him to be the 'Master of St. Agatha', a painter active in Venice in the thirteenth century. Garrison identified him as another Venetian painter of the thirteenth century, the 'Master of the Speaking Christ'.

208 A CRUCIFIXION.
Wood, 18 × 18 cm.

Provenance: D'Atri Collection, Paris.

208 B LAST JUDGEMENT.
Wood, 17 × 19 cm.

Provenance: Private Collection, Milan.

These two panels, as well as three others: the 'Nativity' (Longhi Collection, Florence), the 'Last Supper' and the 'Capture of Christ' (formerly in the Kress Collection, New York), are probably part of the same predella of an altarpiece. The Byzantine influence in the style and iconography is strong in all five panels.

MASTER OF THE VIRGO INTER VIRGINES.

This painter owes his name to one of his works representing the Madonna and Child with four holy virgins in the Rijksmuseum, Amsterdam. Together with Geertgen tot Sint Jans, he was one of the most significant North Netherlands painters in the last quarter of the fifteenth century. He was probably active in Delft. His works express profound earnestness and piety.

209 CRUCIFIXION (CALVARY).
Oak, 78.5 × 58 cm.

The master represented the Crucifixion three times: one large panel is in Barnard Castle (County Durham), one in the Uffizi, Florence, and a third in the Thyssen-Bornemisza Collection. Whereas in the first two representations Christ on the Cross is placed in the central axis, the three crosses in the Lugano panel have been drawn to the right. The foreground is occupied by a group of horsemen and footsoldiers. The painting is distinguished by its dramatic lighting and rendering of the colours. This Crucifixion is datable around 1487, when the art of the Virgo Master had reached its peak.
Provenance: Glitza Collection, Hamburg.

MASTER FROM WESTPHALIA, around 1400.

The attribution of the two panels to a master from Westphalia is due to A. Stange, according to whom the master came from the circle of Konrad von Soest and might be identified as the painter of the Fröndenberg altarpiece, executed between 1410 and 1412.

212 TWO PANELS WITH SYMBOLIC REPRESENTATIONS OF THE VIRGINITY OF MARY AND OF THE SAVIOUR ON THE CROSS.

Left panel: Madonna in the hortus conclusus.
Oak, 28.7 × 18.5 cm.
Inscribed on the halo: 'Sancta maria'.

Right panel: The Saviour on the Cross.
Oak, 28.5 × 18.5 cm.

The Madonna is surrounded by symbols of Mary: the hortus conclusus, the burning bush, the sealed fountain, Gideon's veil, the rose, the ark of the covenant, the closed door of Ezekiel and the altar. The Cross is identified as the 'living cross' by the leafy branches. To the right of Christ is the 'Ecclesia', the Church, represented by a female figure with chalice and banner. In front of her the mystic lamb points at the book, above her the church building. To the left of Christ is a bent, bearded man, blindfolded and bearing a broken banner as symbol of the synagogue. Above him is a skull with the serpent of Eden. A hand appears at each extremity of the Cross: the one above with the key of heaven, the right one blessing, the left one with a sword and the one below beating Death with a hammer.
Provenance: Prince Hohenzollern-Sigmaringen Collection,
Schloss Sigmaringen.

MAZZOLA, Filippo.

* around 1460 in Parma + 1505 in Parma.
Active in Parma as an appreciated portrait painter, he formed his style under the influence of Antonello da Messina and Giovanni Bellini. He was member of a family of painters, and his son Francesco is known as 'Parmigianino'.

213 PORTRAIT OF ALESSANDRO DE RICHAO.
Poplar, 46 × 29 cm.
Inscribed on the parapet: 'ALEX DE RICHAO. FI. M. PAR. P.'.

Venturi, Van Marle and Berenson attributed the painting to Filippo Mazzola and according to Venturi it is one of his best portraits. The quality of the modelling recalls Antonello and the long oval shape of the face is a typical example of Emilian painting.
Provenance: Tietje Collection, Amsterdam.

MEMLING, Hans.

* around 1433 in Seligenstadt near Frankfurt + 1494 in Bruges. Memling is mentioned for the first time when he obtained the citizenship of Bruges in 1465, the documents also registering his place of birth. Judging from his works, he must have received his artistic education in the Netherlands. His thorough knowledge of the forms and pictorial technique of Rogier van der Weyden suggest his having been his pupil. Memling was also a prolific creator of votive paintings and portraits. All his paintings represent an ideal world and testify to his belief in the perfection of the universe.

214 PORTRAIT OF A YOUNG MAN.
Oak, 29 × 22.5 cm.
On the back: still life of a majolica-jug with flowers on a rug.

According to recent research the portrait is part of a triptych with the representation of the Madonna and Child in the central panel and the portrait of the wife on the left. Rogier van der Weyden had already introduced the combination of a votive painting with the double portrait of the married couple as a new form in painting. When the triptych is closed it presents the still life on the back of the portrait of the young man. The representation of flowers has a symbolic meaning and is proof that still life painting appeared in the fifteenth century by way of religion. The white lilies are symbols of the purity of the Virgin, the iris symbolizes Mary as the Queen of Heaven and as Mater Dolorosa. The columbine is the symbol of the Holy Spirit.
Provenance: Duchess of Montrose Collection,
Brodick Castle, Isle of Arran, Scotland.

METSU, Gabriel.

* 1629 in Leiden + 1671 in Amsterdam.
Gerrit Dou in Leiden or Nicolaus Knüpfer in Utrecht are mentioned as his teachers. He became a member of the painters' Guild of Leiden in 1648 and in 1657 he settled in Amsterdam. Gerard Terborch, Pieter de Hooch and Jan Vermeer inspired his later works. The great success of his genre scenes is due to their high pictorial quality and to the gay representation of carefree private life.

215 THE COOK.
Canvas, 37.5 × 31.2 cm.
Signed upper left: 'G. Metsu'.

Like all the people represented in Metsu's paintings, even this cook appears sociable and untroubled. The painting is datable shortly after 1655.
Provenance: A. Preyer Collection, The Hague.

MIERIS, Frans van, the Elder.

* 1635 in Leiden + 1681 in Leiden.
Together with his teacher Gerrit Dou, Frans Mieris the Elder was one of the most significant painters of the Dutch school in the seventeenth century and was particularly appreciated by his contemporaries for his great precision of execution. The Leiden school of 'Feinmalerei', established by Dou, was continued with great ability by Frans Mieris the Elder, and his son Willem as well as his grandson Frans Mieris the Younger ensured that this tradition survived until the late eighteenth century.

216 PORTRAIT OF A LADY.
Oak, 31.5 × 25.5 cm.
Signed and dated lower right: 'F. van Mieris fc. Ao 1672'.

According to Hofstede de Groot this portrait should have as pendant the portrait of a Warrior.
Provenance: Onnes von Nijenrode Collection,
Schloss Nijenrode near Breukelen, Holland.

MOILLON, Louise.

* 1610 in Paris + 1696 in Paris.
Daughter of the painter Nicolas Moillon, who died in 1619, she received her artistic education from her stepfather, the still-life painter François Garnier. She too chose still lifes as her main subject and soon developed her own style, which remained unaltered throughout her life. One of the rare female painters of the period, she was also one of the best representatives of French still-life painting in the seventeenth century.

217 STILL LIFE (FRUIT AND VEGETABLES).
Canvas, 87.5 × 112 cm.
Signed and dated on the stone slab: 'Louys(e) Moillon 1637'.

Due to their simplicity, the still lifes of Louise Moillon correspond to the taste of today. In comparison with the refined, rich representations of her Dutch contemporaries, her compositions appear rather rigid and severe although they are distinguished by sensitive observation and delicacy of execution.

MOR, Anthonis van Dashorst.

* 1519 in Utrecht + between 1576 and 1577 in Antwerp.
The prevailing influence of the portrait groups by Jan van Scorel in his early works suggests that Mor was a pupil of Scorel. In 1547 he is registered as an independent master in the painters' Guild of Antwerp. His presence is documented in Rome, Madrid, Lisbon and London, where he was engaged to paint portraits for princely and royal houses. With the exception of some devotional paintings, he mainly dedicated himself to portraits, in which he achieved great mastery.

217 A PORTRAIT OF JAN BAPTIST CASTILAN.
Wood, 108 × 82.5 cm.

Probably the sitter is the influential Italian artist 'Jean Baptista', with whom Anthonis Mor collaborated for a period. The decoration he is wearing is probably the Order of St. James of Compostela.
Provenance: Sir Otto Beit Collection.

MOMPER, Joos de.

* 1564 in Antwerp + 1635 in Antwerp.
He was a pupil of his father, Bartolomäus de Momper, who had already registered him in the painters' Guild of Antwerp by 1581. His early work is closely related to the tradition of landscape painting established by Pieter Brueghel the Elder. In 1580 Momper probably travelled to Italy through Switzerland and the sight of the Alps had a fundamental influence on his creative activity. He was the most important and most inventive landscape painter in the period of transition from the manneristic style to a more and more naturalistic rendering of landscapes.

218 VIEW OF A PORT WITH MOTIFS OF ROME.
Oak, 50 × 93 cm.
Signed lower left: 'IDM'.

The view belongs to a series of six paintings. On stylistic grounds they appear to be late works and suggest the likelihood of a second journey to Italy. In the background can be seen Castel S. Angelo, a popular Roman subject.
Provenance: Baroness Isbary Collection, Vienna.

219 VIEW OF A VILLAGE ON A RIVER.
Oak, 50 × 93.5 cm.
Signed lower left: 'IDM'.

It belongs to the same series as picture cat. no. 218. The village is probably Treviso. The rendering of the water as a flat surface and the reflection of the opposite bank have such a Dutch effect that one is struck by the Italian buildings.
Provenance: Baroness Isbary Collection, Vienna.

MONTAGNA, Bartolomeo.

* around 1450 in Orzinuovo near Brescia + 1523 in Vicenza. From 1480 apart from short intervals, he is documented as being active in Vicenza. Influenced by Alvise Vivarini, Antonello da Messina and Giovanni Bellini, he nevertheless maintained a style of his own, placing his solemn and somewhat rigid figures against rocky landscapes.

222 SAINT JEROME IN THE WILDERNESS.
Poplar, 40 × 28 cm.

Berenson attributed the picture to Benedetto Rusconi. The second figure, that of the kneeling saint, appeared after cleaning.

MOSTAERT, Jan.

* around 1472-1473 in Haarlem + 1555 or 1556 in Haarlem. According to Mander, Mostaert's teacher may have been Jacob van Haarlem, probably a member of the circle of Geertgen tot Sint Jans. For eighteen years he was court painter to the Governess Margaret of Austria in Mechlin. Although he acquired the outward characteristics of the Renaissance, Mostaert remained true to the guarded and reserved style of the Haarlem tradition. Among his various paintings, his portraits are now particularly appreciated.

224 REDEEMED SOULS AT THE APPEARANCE OF CHRIST IN LIMBO WITH FEMALE DONOR.
Oak, 24 × 16 cm.

The panel is the right wing of a diptych, the left one with the representation of the Resurrected Christ in Limbo is in the Rijksmuseum of Enschede. The female donor in the foreground, probably by another hand, may be Mary of Burgundy, mother of the Governess Margaret and wife of Maximilian of Austria.

225 THE BANISHMENT OF HAGAR.
Oak, 94 × 131 cm.

In the foreground Abraham is sending Hagar, Sarah's servant, and the young Ismael, the son she had borne him, into the desert of Berseba. In the background small figures illustrate what happened before and after the banishment. (Genesis 21).
Provenance: Dr Oertel Collection, Munich.

MUELICH (MIELICH), Hans.

* 1516 in Munich + 1573 in Munich.
Belonging to a family of painters documented in Munich from 1500, he learned his craft in the workshop of his father, the town-painter Wolfgang Muelich. In 1536 he joined Albrecht Altdorfer in Regensburg and in 1541 he went to Rome. He was principally a portraitist.

226 PORTRAIT OF A WOMAN AGED 57.
Wood, 71 × 53.5 cm.
Signed and dated on the left edge: 'HM. 1539'. Above the sitter, the inscription: 'MEINES ALTERS IM. 57. IAR'.

The Muelich portraits follow a fixed pattern: the sitters are represented seated or standing, hip length and at a slight angle. An inscription or a coat of arms decorates the wall in the background.
Provenance: Count J. S. Tryskiewicz Collection,
Château de Birre, France.

MURILLO, Bartolomé Esteban.

* 1618 in Seville + 1682 in Seville.
Murillo, as the youngest of fourteen children and orphan at the age of ten, soon knew hardship and need. On account of his exceptional gift for drawing he became a pupil of Juan de Castillo. A presence in Madrid, although not documented, might explain the influence of Rubens and of van Dyck in his works. Murillo used engravings after Italian, Flemish, French and German works for his compositions. Particularly appreciated by the clergy, he painted a great number of Madonnas, Immaculate Conceptions and other religious subjects. He was influenced in his early works by Zurbarán and later by Ribera; then in the years around 1650 by Rubens and van Dyck.

227 SAINT JUSTA.
Canvas, 95 × 67.5 cm.

The painting is a companion piece to the St. Rufina still at Stafford House in London. Justa and Rufina, patron saints of Seville, daughters of a town potter, refused to sell their vases to the pagans for the feast of Adonis and were martyred. The painting represents the late style of the master and is to be dated around 1675-1678.
Provenance: Duke of Sutherland Collection,
Stafford House, London.

228 THE MADONNA AND SAINTS APPEARING TO SAINT ROSE.
Canvas, 190 × 147 cm.

St. Rose, an influential Franciscan tertiary, lived in Viterbo towards the middle of the thirteenth century. According to the story of her life, she was cured of a serious illness due to a vision of the Madonna, the scene represented by Murillo. The saint preaching one of her celebrated sermons is represented in the background. This painting, executed around 1666-1668, is a significant work of Murillo's best period.
Provenance: Contini-Bonacossi Collection, Florence.

NATTIER, Jean-Marc.

* 1685 in Paris + 1766 in Paris.
Son of a portrait painter, he was probably a pupil of Jean Jouvenet. In 1717 he made his name when he portrayed Peter the Great and Catherine I of Russia in Amsterdam. The elegance of his style and his brilliant colours led to his success as a portraitist at the court of Louis XV, where from 1745 he was court painter.

229 MADAME BOURET AS DIANA.
Canvas, 138 × 105 cm.
Signed and dated on a stone lower right: 'Nattier pinxit 1745'.

Nattier chose to represent ladies with the attributes of goddesses or as allegories of the four seasons or the four elements. On account of this flattering disguise and his disposition to idealize the sitters, embellishing their features, Nattier became the favourite painter of female portraits.
Provenance: Madame Dupuy Collection, Paris.

NEEFS, Pieter the Elder.

* around 1578 in Antwerp + 1660 in Antwerp.
Neefs owes his reputation to church interiors distinguished by the detailed precision of the design and by a special luminosity. The figures in his pictures were for the most part painted by T. Francken the Younger and by David Teniers.

230 A INTERIOR OF A GOTHIC CHURCH.
Wood, 39 × 68.5 cm.
Dated on an old inscription on the back: '1610'.

Pieter Neefs the Elder represented three different types of always varying church interior: the three-nave Gothic church, the seven-nave strongly varying church interior, and the church interior with a brightly-lit chapel in the foreground. The painting in this collection belongs to the first type.

NEER, Aert van der.

* 1603 or 1604 in Gorkum near Dordrecht + 1677 in Amsterdam.
In his early years the painter was a steward in Gorkum. In 1634 he settled in Amsterdam, where he began to paint and was also a part-time innkeeper. He specialized in painting landscapes at sunrise or sunset and with moonlight. Particularly in his winter scenes he attained delicate luminous effects and colour harmony. Due to the picturesque quality of his landscapes, van der Neer is to be considered one of the leading masters of Dutch painting in the second half of the seventeenth century.

230 EVENING LANDSCAPE WITH FISHING BOATS.
Oak, 30 × 45 cm.

From the luminous river the eye is led towards the depth of the painting drawn by the brightness of the sinking sun, passing over the willow tree in the foreground, the small boat on the left and along the tongue of land on the right to the nearest boat.
Provenance: Countess de Maillé Collection, Paris.

231 LANDSCAPE IN MOONLIGHT.
Wood, 36 × 60.5 cm.

The painting again illustrates the painter's preference for light reflected on water. Datable around 1645.

232 WINTER LANDSCAPE.
Canvas, 36.5 × 45 cm.

A somewhat harsh appearance is created by the whiteness of the snow and by the clouds lacking a billowy effect, thus avoiding a false Romanticism despite the pictorial details.
Provenance: Count Schönborn-Buchheim Collection, Vienna.

234 LANDSCAPE AT SUNSET.
Wood, 41.5 × 60.5 cm.
Signed on the lower right: 'AV DN'.

Van der Neer has painted this delicate landscape with great restraint. Characteristic is the way in which the sunlight is reflected in the water.

NETSCHER, Caspar.

* 1636 in Heidelberg + 1684 in The Hague.
From 1655 he was a pupil of Gerard Terborch in Deventer (Netherlands). In 1659 he is documented in Bordeaux, where he married; he returned to The Hague with his family in 1662. He was an appreciated painter of genre scenes and of portraits. The delicacy of his painting and the precision of the drawing distinguish his pictures.

235 PORTRAIT OF A GENTLEMAN.
Canvas, 53.5 × 44 cm.
Signed and dated centre right: 'C. Netscher 1676'.

236 PORTRAIT OF A LADY.
Canvas, 54.3 × 45.5 cm.
Signed and dated centre right: 'C. Netscher 1676'.

The two portraits are companion pieces. The gentleman is wearing the full-bottomed wig fashionable towards the end of the seventeenth century. His cravat and cuffs and the trimming of the lady's gown are of a precious needlepoint lace, 'point de France'.

NICCOLÒ DI TOMMASO.

Painter of the Florentine school, he is documented between 1343 and 1376 in Florence, where he probably died in 1405. He was mainly influenced by Nardo di Cione. Of his works the frescoes in the Ospizio di S. Antonio in Pistoia and the altarpieces in the museums of Naples and Florence are preserved.

237 MADONNA WITH SAINTS AND ANGELS;
ABOVE: CHRIST BLESSING.
Poplar, gabled, 87 × 35 cm.

Voss attributed the panel to Nardo di Cione, Berenson to Giovanni del Biondo, whereas Gronau and Offner ascribed it ot Niccolò di Tommaso.
Provenance: Josef Cremer Collection, Dortmund.

OCHTERVELT, Jacob.

The dates of his life are uncertain. Between 1655 and 1672 he is documented in Rotterdam; in 1674 he was in Amsterdam. He must have died before 1710, the year his widow was buried in Rotterdam. According to Houbraken, Ochtervelt and Pieter de Hooch were pupils of Nicolas Berchem. He painted mainly genre scenes in rich bourgeois interiors.

238 THE OYSTER EATERS.
Oak, 47 × 37.5 cm.

The young woman with the wineglass and Delft jug and the man playing the lute are figures often chosen as models by Ochtervelt. He tended to place them against the dark background of an interior in order to enhance the colours of the costumes. Executed around 1667-1669.
Provenance: Six Collection, Amsterdam.

ORLEY, Bernaert van.

* around 1488 in Brussels + 1541 in Brussels.
He belonged to a family of painters and may have received his first artistic education from his father, Valentin van Orley. By 1515 he was already active at the court of Margaret of Austria, Regent of the Netherlands, becoming in 1518 court painter, a position he also retained under the Regent Mary of Hungary despite difficulties on account of his conversion to Protestantism. Bernaert van Orley is regarded as one of the leading representatives of Renaissance art in Flanders.

239 REST ON THE FLIGHT.
Oak, 87 × 72 cm.

Orley took as his model for this panel the woodcut of this same subject by Lucas Cranach the Elder, dated 1509. Joseph and the donkey have hardly been changed, whereas the figures of Mary and the Child as well as the landscape differ widely from the model.
Provenance: Baron Detlev von Hadeln Collection, Florence.

OSTADE, Adriaen van.

* 1610 in Haarlem + 1685 in Haarlem.
According to Houbraken, Adriaen van Ostade and Adriaen Brouwer were pupils of Frans Hals. The early works of Ostade, however, reveal only the influence of Brouwer. After 1640, showing the influence of Rembrandt, he achieved a deep, warm chiaroscuro. Ostade mostly represented peasants and simple country folk, their life and pleasures.

240 MEN IN THE TAVERN.
Oak, 32.3 × 24.6 cm.
Signed and dated lower right: 'AV Ostade 1661'.

In his early paintings Ostade preferred modest interiors with the quickly moving figures of coarse peasants. Around 1660 he gave preference, as in this painting, to quiet figures and small contemplative groups. In contrast to the early caricature-like models, these figures are represented as true to life individuals.
Provenance: Max von Goldschmidt-Rothschild Collection, Frankfurt.

OSTADE, Isaac van.

* 1621 in Haarlem + 1649 in Haarlem.
Isaac van Ostade was a pupil of his elder brother Adriaen, who particularly influenced him in his early paintings of abattoir and peasant scenes. After 1640 he gave preference to rural scenes and illustrated the life of peasants in the streets, in courtyards and outside traverns. He must have been a tireless artist as he left a considerable number of paintings when he died at the age of only 28. In the catalogue of his works Hofstede de Groot listed more than 350 paintings.

241 REST OUTSIDE A FARMHOUSE.
Oak, 48 × 40 cm.
Signed and dated below on the door: 'Isaak v. Ostade 1649'.

Painted in the year of his death, this painting reveals the perfection attained by the master during his short life.
Provenance: Sir Alfred Beit Collection, Dublin.

PACHER, Michael.

* around 1435 probably in Bruneck in the Pusteria valley, South Tyrol + 1498 in Salzburg.

Painter and wood carver of exceptional ability, he probably learned his craft from a Tyrolese master and journeyed to Northern Italy to Andrea Mantegna and Giovanni Bellini. The most significant painter of Late Gothic art in the Alpine regions. Jan Polack and the painters of the 'Donauschule' came under his influence.

242 MADONNA ENTHRONED WITH SAINTS CATHERINE AND MARGARET.

Pine, 167 × 77.2 cm.

Originally the panel was in the Benedictine Abbey of St. Peter in Salzburg, probably as the central panel of a narrow altarpiece. The attribution to Michael Pacher himself is disputed and the painter of the panel may have been a younger member of the Pacher workshop. Against a gold background is the Madonna with the Child putting the ring on the finger of St. Catherine. To the right of the Madonna is St. Margaret holding the cross with which she defeated the dragon. Two angels are crowning the Mother of God.

Provenance: Benedictine Abbey of St. Peter, Salzburg.

PALMA VECCHIO (Jacopo d'Antonio Negreti).

* around 1480 in Serina near Bergamo + 1528 in Venice.
From 1510 Palma is documented in Venice, where he lived until his death. He received his first artistic education from the Bergamask painters resident in Venice. The influence of Giorgione determined his style. Palma had a leading position in the development of Venetian painting, and according to Cavalcaselle 'he shares with Giorgione and Titian the honour of having modernized and regenerated Venetian art'.

243 SACRA CONVERSAZIONE.
Madonna and Child with SS. Mary Magdalen, John the Baptist, Catherine and a Donor.
Panel transferred to canvas, 105 × 136 cm.

The portrayed donor and commissioner of the painting is probably Francesco Priuli. In his guide 'Venezia città nobilissima' published in 1581, Francesco Sansovino described the painting in the Palazzo Priuli. It was executed around 1515-1520 when Palma Vecchio was inspired by Titian's style.
Provenance: Duke of Leuchtenberg Collection,
Schloss Seeon, Chiemsee.

244 PORTRAIT OF A YOUNG WOMAN,
CALLED 'LA BELLA'.
Canvas, 95 × 80 cm.
Inscribed on the stone parapet: 'A.M.B./ND.'.

Palma's representations of beautiful women, preferably half-length, are his finest creations; of these 'La Bella' is one of the most beautiful and splendid examples. It was executed around 1512. The inscription has not been deciphered.
Provenance: Baron Edouard de Rothschild Collection, Paris.

PATENIER, Joachim.

* around 1480 in Dinant + 1524 in Antwerp.
Nothing is known about the early years or the artistic education of Patenier. Several scholars assume an apprenticeship with Gerard David in Bruges. In 1515 he was resident in Antwerp. He soon made a name for himself in Europe due to his beautiful landscapes. Dürer must have appreciated him, mentioning him in his diary as 'the good landscape painter'. Patenier succeeded in lifting landscape painting from a secondary position to that of an autonomous art form.

245 LANDSCAPE WITH THE REST ON THE FLIGHT INTO EGYPT.
Oak, 31.5 × 57.5 cm.

In the centre foreground the Madonna and Child are sitting near a spring, in front of which is an iris in bloom, symbol of the Passion; in the background Joseph is picking fruit; on the far left the donkey is grazing. According to Friedländer the Madonna is painted by Patenier himself, while in many of Patenier's landscapes the figures were added by different masters. The painting is datable around 1510.
Provenance: Eduard Simon Collection, Berlin.

PATER, Jean-Baptiste-Joseph.

* 1695 in Valenciennes + 1736 in Paris.
Son of the sculptor Antoine Pater and pupil of Watteau. Although a successful painter of 'fêtes galantes', his best works are those representing military scenes and bathing women. An indefatigable worker, he died at the early age of 40 on account of overwork.

246 CONCERT CHAMPÊTRE.
Canvas, 52.5 × 68 cm.
Signed and dated on the base of the column: 'Pater 1734'.

Pater painted several versions of this scene as he did of most of his compositions. The delicate, transparent atmospheric veil over the landscape distinguishes his paintings from those of Watteau and Lancret.
Provenance: J. Pierpont Morgan Collection, New York.

PESNE, Antoine.

* 1683 in Paris + 1757 in Paris.
He received his artistic education from his father, from his great uncle Charles de Lafosse and at the Royal Academy, where in 1703 he was awarded the Prix de Rome. Between 1705 and 1710 he studied in Venice and Rome. In 1710 he was called to Berlin and appointed court painter, a position retained under three successive Kings of Prussia; he was particularly esteemed by Frederick the Great. He owes his historical importance to his having introduced the French style of painting into Germany and also to the fact that in 1732 he founded the Prussian Academy.

247 BOY WITH A MASK.
Oak, 57 × 44 cm.

The painting reveals strong Venetian influence, particularly that of Piazzetta, and might have been executed during his Venetian period, prior to 1710.
Provenance: August the Strong Collection, Dresden.

PIER FRANCESCO FIORENTINO.

Priest and painter, active in Florence in the last decades of the fifteenth century. A pupil and follower of Benozzo Gozzoli, he was influenced by Fra Filippo and Castagno.

248 B ADORATION OF THE CHILD.
Poplar, 90 × 75 cm.

Provenance: F. Graham Collection, London, on loan from Countess Batthyany-Thyssen.

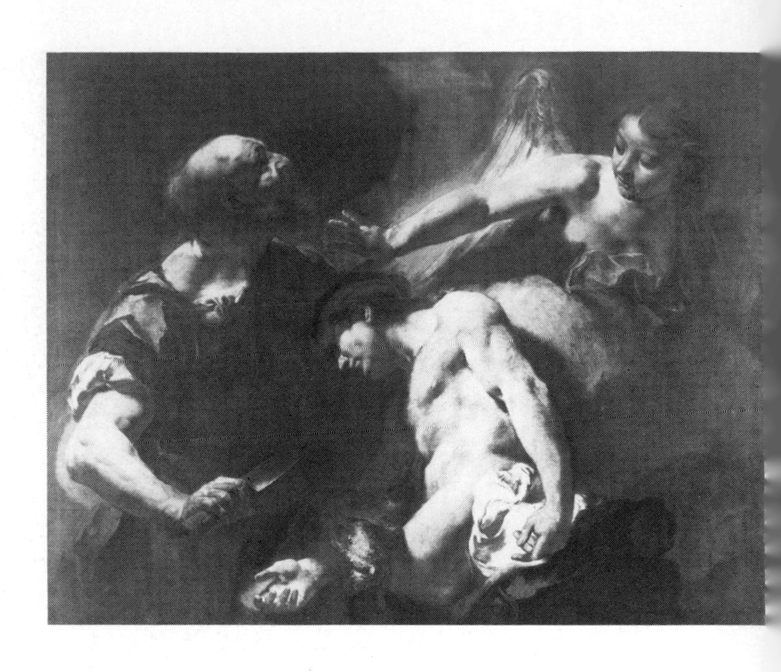

PIAZZETTA, Giovanni Battista.

* 1682 in Venice + 1754 in Venice.
Piazzetta was the son of a wood carver, and was at first trained as such by his father before he dedicated himself to painting. After his apprenticeship to Antonio Molinari he went to Bologna, where he studied the works of the Carracci and of Guercino and entered the workshop of Crespi. In 1711 he returned to Venice. Due to his conscientious and scrupulous technique his paintings were limited in number; nevertheless he had a lasting influence on Venetian culture in the eighteenth century.

248 C SACRIFICE OF ABRAHAM.
Canvas, 102 × 127 cm.

The painting was executed around 1715, shortly after Piazzetta's return from Bologna and reveals the strong influence of Crespi.
Provenance: Fenwick-Owen Collection, London.

PIERO DELLA FRANCESCA.

* between 1410 and 1420 in Borgo San Sepolcro, Arezzo
+ 1492 in Borgo San Sepolcro.
The painter is documented for the first time in 1439 as working with Domenico Veneziano on the frescoes in the choir of S. Egidio in Florence. Piero della Francesca was inspired not only by Domenico Veneziano but also by Paolo Uccello and Fra Angelico. He received commissions from Federico da Montefeltro, Duke of Urbino, and from Lionello d'Este of Ferrara. The cycle of frescoes in S. Francesco at Arezzo with scenes from the legend of the True Cross is his most important work still preserved. The artistic importance of Piero has only recently been recognized and he is today considered one of the most important masters of the Renaissance.

249 PORTRAIT OF GUIDOBALDO DA MONTEFELTRO.
Poplar, 41 × 27.5 cm.

An inscription indicating the painting as a portrait of Raphael at the age of six, painted by his father Giovanni Santi, had already been doubted prior to a recent cleaning that proved it to be of a later date. The sitter has been identified as Guidobaldo da Montefeltro on account of the portrait on a medal of 1483 created to mark the investiture of the latter as Duke of Urbino and of his portrait by Justus von Gent in Windsor Castle. Hendy, H. Focillon and P. de Vecchi are concordant in attributing the painting to Piero della Francesca.
Provenance: Leopold Hirsch Collection, London.

PIETRO DA RIMINI.

Painter of the Rimini school, active in the first half of the fourteenth century in Romagna, in Veneto and in the Marches. He painted mainly altarpieces and frescoes, and is close to Giovanni Baronzio, to whom several of his works were formerly attributed.

249 A NATIVITY.
Poplar, 17.2 × 19.7 cm.

The painting represents: the birth of Christ, the announcement to the shepherds, the arrival of the Magi, the two legendary midwives Salome and Zelomi bathing the Christ Child and Joseph's vision. This panel together with an 'Entombment of Christ' in the Staatliche Museen, Berlin, and its companion piece the 'Presentation in the Temple', probably belong to the same predella, dated 1335.
Provenance: G. H. Dixon Collection, England.

PIERO DI COSIMO (Piero di Lorenzo).

* around 1462 + 1521.
Painter of the Florentine school. Documented in 1480 in the workshop of Cosimo Rosselli, where Albertinelli and Fra Bartolomeo were his companions. Inspired by Leonardo, he had a lasting influence on his pupils Andrea del Sarto and Pontormo. His religious representations were frequently imitated by minor contemporaries.

250 MADONNA AND CHILD WITH ANGELS.
Poplar, tondo, diam. 78 cm.

Zeri pointed out the closeness of the painting to a similar representation by Piero di Cosimo, the 'Madonna with music-making Angels' in the Cini Collection in Venice. He attributed the tondo to Jacopo di Domenico Toschi, dating it between 1500 and 1510.

PITTONI, Giovanni Battista.

* 1687 in Venice + 1767 in Venice.
Descending from a family of painters, engravers and architects, he was first a pupil of his uncle, Francesco Pittoni, and later entered the workshop of Antonio Balestra, with whom he remained for a period in Rome and in Emilia. Together with Giovanni Battista Tiepolo and Piazzetta he renewed Venetian painting, freeing it from the heavy forms of Baroque. Due to his refined, fresh style and to the elegance and delicacy of his shapes, he became a typical representative of Rococo.

250 A HOLY FAMILY.
Canvas, 108 × 135 cm.

The gesture of the hands, the rhythm of the movements, the folds of the robes, the angled stance of the figures, the fluid rendering of the outlined profiles are typical elements of Pittoni's painting, chosen intentionally to express great vivacity and to suggest a dramatic atmosphere.

PIRRI, Antonio di Manfredo da Bologna.

The painter is mentioned in just one written document indicating his presence in Naples in 1511. Only two signed works by him are known: one in the Poldi Pezzoli Museum in Milan and another in Turin. Their pictorial quality indicates the influence of Francesco Francia and Bernardo Zaganelli. According to Venturi the intensity of his colours and the delicate facial design are of Ferrarese origin and place him in this school. Other art critics indicate a Venetian influence, particularly in his late period.

250 C SAINT FRANCIS RECEIVING THE STIGMATA.
Canvas, 42.5 × 54.5 cm.

Comparison with the two paintings signed by Pirri confirms his authorship and a dating around 1520. In the painting of the Thyssen-Bornemisza Collection new elements further the former knowledge of Pirri's work: the pictorial effect of the meadows in the far distance and of the watercourse would seem to confirm the artist's connection with Venice.

POLACK, Jan.

* around 1435 probably in Cracow + 1519 in Munich.
Active in Munich from 1479 where he had a large workshop, in 1488 he was appointed town painter. The leading master of Late Gothic painting in the town, he received commissions mainly for altarpieces and frescoes. The influence of the Franconian school of painting on his work is evident, particularly that of Hans Pleydenwurff and Michael Wolgemut.

251 PORTRAIT OF A MAN.
Wood, 29.5 × 17 cm.

E. Buchner dated the portrait around 1480. According to Salm the portrait probably represents a member of the 'Bauhütte' of the Liebfrauenkirche of Munich, as portraits by Polack similar in style and size were identified as portraits of the master builder and of the master carpenter of the 'Bauhütte'.

252 PORTRAIT OF A BENEDICTINE ABBOT.
Pine, 57.3 × 41 cm.
Dated on the upper edge: '14 84'.

The sitter has the attributes of St. Benedict: the broken glass with the serpent, indicating the attempt of the monks of Vicovaro to poison the saint, and the open book, the Rule of St. Benedict.
Provenance: Baron von Bissing Collection, Munich.

PONTORMO, Jacopo Carucci, called.

* 1494 in Pontormo near Florence + 1556 in Florence.
He received his artistic education in Florence from Leonardo, Albertinelli, Piero di Cosimo and Andrea del Sarto, who particularly influenced him. His frescoes in the cloister of the Certosa del Galluzzo were inspired by Dürer's engravings. After 1530 Pontormo became closely connected with Michelangelo, who influenced him fundamentally.

253 PORTRAIT OF A LADY.
Poplar, 101 × 78.5 cm.

The social postion as well as the character of the lady are represented by the expression of noble reserve and the well balanced composition. The portrait is dated around 1530-1535.
Provenance: von Dirksen Collection, Berlin.

POST, Frans Jansz.

* around 1612 in Leiden + 1680 in Haarlem.
Post accompanied Prince Johann Maurits of Nassau in the region of Pernambuco in Brazil between 1637 and 1644. In 1646 after his return to Haarlem he became a member of the painters' Guild. Using the impressions of his journey he specialized in tropical landscapes, still preserved in great number.

254 FARM WITH 'CASA-GRANDE' IN BRAZIL.
Oak, 37 × 54 cm.
Signed and dated lower right: 'F. Post 1656'.

Post represented a typical 'aldeia', an estate in the interior. On the left is the 'casa-grande', the fortified residence of the owner of the plantation; on the right, the quarters of the slaves and workers; in the background the fertile plain where mainly sugar was grown.

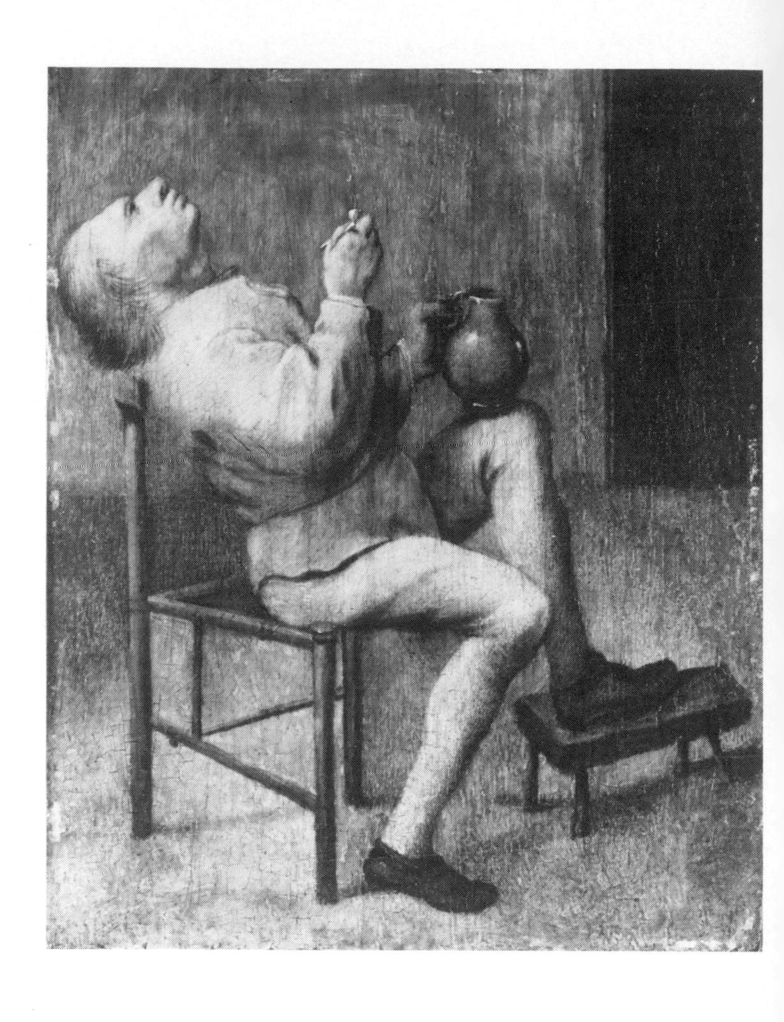

QUAST, Pieter Jansz.

* around 1605-1606 in Amsterdam + 1647 in Amsterdam.
Quast was active in The Hague and in Amsterdam. His paintings mostly represent scenes from the life of peasants and appear strongly influenced by Adriaen Brouwer. His coarse figures are always close to caricatures.

256 THE SMOKER.
Oak, 19.5 × 16 cm.

The Suermondt Museum in Aachen owns a second version of this composition. Hofstede de Groot first attributed the two paintings to A. Brouwer and later to Quast. Although the panel is certainly not a work of Brouwer, the attribution to Quast is not entirely convincing, either.

RAPHAEL, Raffaello Santi.

* 1483 in Urbino + 1520 in Rome.
Probably introduced to painting by his father, Giovanni Santi, court painter in Urbino, as a child Raphael was already in close touch with the works of important masters in the Palace of Urbino. In 1497 he entered the workshop of Perugino, the most appreciated Umbrian master of the time. Arriving in Florence in 1504, he was particularly impressed by the art of Leonardo and Michelangelo. In 1508 Pope Julius II called him to Rome and commissioned the frescoes in his apartments of the Vatican. In the same year Raphael began his activity as an architect with the project for the Farnesina. After Bramante's death in 1514, Pope Leo X appointed him superintendent of the construction of St. Peter's. Despite his early death he left a rich opus, for centuries admired and discussed as a classical ideal.

259 PORTRAIT OF A YOUNG MAN (Alessandro de' Medici ?). Poplar, 44 × 29.4 cm.

Van Regteren Altena identified the sitter as Alessandro de' Medici (1505-1537), the illegitimate son of Lorenzo de' Medici, Duke of Urbino, attributing to Raphael the painting for long ascribed to Giulio Romano. After recent cleaning Hendy also accepted the portrait as a late work by Raphael.

REMBRANDT, Harmensz van Rijn.

* 1606 in Leiden + 1669 in Amsterdam.
As the son of a miller, Rembrandt belonged to the rising lower middle class, and after attending the Latin school and University, he first became a pupil in Leiden of Jacob Swanenburgh, the painter of historical subjects, and then of Pieter Lastman in Amsterdam. He set up as an independant painter in Leiden in 1625, depicting religious or classical subjects in Lastman's style. In 1531 he settled in Amsterdam, where until the fifties he was artistically and financially successful, and became one of the most important portrait painters of all times. In 1656, on account of his extravagant way of life and despite the number of important commissions, he was so deeply in debt that his house and property were auctioned. From then on he lived in private with his son Titus and his servant Hendrickje Stoffels; as commissions for portraits were lacking, he painted biblical scenes, and self-portraits, some of his most important works. About 600 paintings, over 300 etchings, and more than 1500 drawings by Rembrandt are still preserved.

260 STORMY LANDSCAPE.
Oak, 22 × 29.5 cm.

Rembrandt dedicated himself to landscape painting, at first close to Seghers, only in the late 1630's. The landscape of about 1640 in the Thyssen-Bornemisza Collection represents an important step towards the achievement of his own style. The dramatic drift of the clouds, the melancholic atmosphere and the figures are elements typical of Rembrandt.
Provenance: Earl of Northbrook Collection, London.

259 B SELF-PORTRAIT.
Wood, 72.5 × 58.5 cm.

Rembrandt's personality is most apparent in his numerous self-portraits, as if the master were searching for his true ego. The companion piece to this portrait is the one of his wife, Saskia, completed by Rembrandt after her death in 1643, also the approximate date of the self-portrait.
Provenance: W. Buckley Collection, Basingstoke, England.

REMBRANDT, SCHOOL OF.

260 A PORTRAIT OF A LADY WITH RUFF.
Oak, 64 × 51 cm.
Dated lower right: '1644'.

REYMERSWAELE, Marinus van.

The painter may be one and the same as 'Moryn Claessone, Zeelander', who was an apprentice of a glass painter in Antwerp in 1509. As his name indicates, he might thus have been born around 1490 in Reymerswall in South Beveland (Zeeland), later destroyed by a flood. A 'Marinus Claessoen, born in Romers wael', is mentioned in a judgement of 1567 pronounced in Middelburg on account of having participated in iconoclastic activities. Marinus van Reymerswaele belonged to the followers of Quinten Matsys and gave preference to scenes of men surrounded by books, papers and documents. He was influenced by Leonardo and Dürer.

261 THE CALLING OF SAINT MATTHEW.
Oak, 71 × 88 cm.

On the wall a small tablet with biblical citations: Mat. 9.9; Mar. 2.14; Luc. 5f[27]. Of the many known versions of this composition, testifying to its popularity, the autograph version in the Thyssen-Bornemisza Collection is by far the best. The work illustrates the change from religious to genre painting.
Provenance: Earl of Northbrook Collection, London.

RICCI, Sebastiano.

* 1659 in Belluno + 1734 in Venice.
Pupil of Sebastiano Mazzoni in Venice and of Giovanni del Sole in Bologna, during his early years he received commissions in a number of different places: in 1685 in Parma, subsequently in Rome and Naples; in 1695 he went to Florence, Bologna, Modena, Parma and Milan; in 1700 he returned to Venice; in 1701-1703 he is documented in Vienna, in 1704 in Venice, in 1706-1707 in Florence; between 1709 and 1716 he was active in London and for a short time in the Netherlands and Paris. In 1717 he settled in Venice and attained notable success in the last years of his life.

262 B SAINT MAGDALEN COMFORTED BY ANGELS.
Canvas, 147 × 112.5 cm.

Pallucchini points out the influence of Roman Baroque particularly apparent in this painting, dating it around 1694-1695, a period Ricci spent in Rome.
Provenance: Palazzo Soranzo-Venier-Van Axel-Barozzi, Venice.

ROBERT, Hubert.

* 1733 in Paris + 1808 in Paris.
His connections with people of influence led to his going to Rome in 1754 to study at the French Academy, where he applied himself to the art of Piranesi and Pannini, painters of ancient ruins. He returned to Paris in 1765 with a collection of drawings rich enough to serve as inspiration for the rest of his life. Admitted to the Académie Royale, his great artistic achievement was recognized and he earned great merit for his part in the creation of the Musée du Louvre.

263 THE FOOTBRIDGE.
Canvas, oval, 59 × 47 cm.

Unlike those of Watteau and Fragonard, Robert's figures are only enlivening elements in the landscape; the rendering of light and atmosphere add particular charm. Datable around 1775.
Provenance: Count Gabriel du Tillet Collection.

ROBERTI, Ercole de'.

* around 1450 in Ferrara + 1496 in Ferrara.
Together with Cosmé Tura and Francesco del Cossa, Ercole de' Roberti is the third leading master of the quattrocento in Ferrara. Pupil and follower of his famous predecessors, he softened their severe style and enriched their colourscheme under the influence of Giovanni Bellini. He followed Cossa to Bologna, collaborating with him on frescoes and altarpieces. In 1486 he succeeded Tura as court painter to the Este family in Ferrara, retaining this position until his death.

264 THE ARGONAUTS LEAVING COLCHIS.
Walnut, 35 × 26.5 cm.

The painting belongs to a series of representations from the legend of the Argonauts, other panels are to be found in museums in Padua and Paris and in private collections in Florence and England. The choice of wood shows that the panels must have decorated a wedding chest, probably part of a group painted by Ercole de' Roberti for the wedding of Isabella d'Este. To be dated around 1480.
Provenance: F. B. Gutmann Collection,
Heemstede, Haarlem.

RUBENS, Peter Paul.

* 1577 in Siegen + 1640 in Antwerp.
He learned his craft with Tobias Verhaecht, Adam von Noort and Otto Venius, and from 1598 was an independent master in Antwerp. His position as court painter to Duke Vincenzo Gonzaga in Mantua from 1600 to 1608, leading him to Venice, Turin, Rome and Spain, was of particular importance for his artistic development. Returning to Antwerp in 1608, he was recognized as the leading master of Flemish painting and chosen by the Archduke Albert as his court painter in 1609. The same year he married Isabella Brant, who died in 1626. Around 1622 he began a particularly active period of his life, travelling on diplomatic and artistic missions to France, Holland, Spain and England. As ambassador extraordinary he conducted peace negotiations between Spain and England. The last ten years of his life were brightened by his second marriage in 1630 to the sixteen-year-old Helena Fourment, who bore him five children.

266 THE TOILETTE OF VENUS.
Canvas, 137 × 111 cn.

Among the numerous copies of great artists executed by Rubens, the eleven copies after Titian have a particular importance and document the close affinity between the two great masters. Titian painted the popular classical theme of Venus and Cupid at least three times in different versions, of which the only original variant is preserved in the National Gallery in Washington. The version used by Rubens as his model, in 1628-1629 in the collection of Philip II in Madrid, is lost.
Provenance: Ch. Léon Cardon Collection, Brussels.

267 VIRGIN AND CHILD WITH SAINT ELIZABETH AND INFANT JOHN.
Canvas, 151 × 113 cm.

Stylistic reasons suggest a date around 1618. The subject was frequently repeated by Rubens. His two sons, Albert and Nicolas, were probably the models for the two children and also appear in other representations as does the old woman in the background, here St. Elizabeth.
Provenance: Earl of Lonsdale Collection,
Lowther Castle, Penrith, Cumberland.

268 SAINT MICHAEL OVERTHROWING LUCIFER AND THE REBELLIOUS ANGELS.

Canvas, 149 × 128 cm.

On stylistic grounds a date around 1635 is likely. Variants of the same subject occupied Rubens from 1620 and in 1622 he executed the famous 'Fall of the Angels', now in the Alte Pinakothek in Munich. The figure of Lucifer is taken from an earlier drawing of about 1614-1615. This painting is his most mature and last representation of the subject.

RUISDAEL, Jacob Isaacz van.

* 1628 or 1629 in Haarlem + 1682 probably in Amsterdam.
His first artistic education was presumably as a pupil of his father, Isaac van Ruisdael, and his early paintings also reveal the noticeable influence of his uncle, Salomon, and of the landscape painter Cornelisz Vroom from Haarlem. Jacob was admitted to the painters' Guild in Haarlem in 1648; from 1657 he was resident in Amsterdam with Meindert Hobbema as his pupil. In 1676 he was registered in Amsterdam as a physician, having taken his degree at Caen. He painted landscapes of hills, woods and flatlands, seascapes, winter and shore scenes, distiguished by a moving and melancholy atmosphere. Jacob Isaacz is the best known member of the Ruisdael family of painters.

269 VIEW OF NAARDEN, THE MUIDERBERG AND THE ZUIDERZEE.
Oak, 35 × 66 cm.
Signed and dated lower left: 'J. Ruisdael 1647'.

The painting is exceptional as an early work on account of the flat landscape seen from above, his favourite subject only after 1660. The ray of light in the centre indicates the influence of Rembrandt and the long and narrow shape of the panel may derive from early landscapes of Seghers and van Goyen. Typical of Ruisdael is the rendering of depth by means of the path winding away from the foreground into the far distance.
Provenance: Lady Theodora Guest Collection, London.

270 FLAT LANDSCAPE WITH CORNFIELDS NEAR THE ZUIDERZEE.
Canvas, 45 × 56 cm.

Flat landscapes, rare among his early paintings, have an important place in his later work. The sense of space is created by the contrast of chiaroscuro and the extension of the different zones is determined by the winding path and the size of the figures; the sunlight has a space-building effect. The model for this landscape is the coast of the Zuiderzee, near Naarden. To be dated around 1660-1662.
Provenance: W. H. C. Tietje Collection, Amsterdam.

271 BLEACHING FIELDS NEAR HAARLEM.
Canvas, 33.7 × 41.8 cm.
Signed and dated lower right: 'JvR 1660'.

The views over flat landscape seen from above appear frequently in the work of Ruisdael after 1660 and are generally views of Haarlem. This kind of painting was already known as 'Een Haarlempje van Ruisdael' during his lifetime, and was imitated by Jan van Kessel and Jan Vermeer. This is the only dated 'Haarlempje' (view of Haarlem).
Provenance: W. A. Slater Collection, Washington.

272 VIEW OF HAARLEM WITH THE HUIS TER KLEEF IN THE FOREGROUND.
Canvas, 50.8 × 63.3 cm.
Signed lower left: 'J v Ruisdael'.

The great depth and sense of space suggest a date around 1670. The focal point in the background is the Groote Kerk (St. Bavo) of Haarlem. The castle in the foreground was used by the Spaniards as headquarters during the siege of Haarlem in 1572-1573. Provenance: Earl of Abingdon Collection, Wytham Abbey.

273 WINTER LANDSCAPE.
Canvas, 65.6 × 96.7 cm.
Signed lower right: 'J v Ruisdael'.

The snowball fight in the foreground contrasts with the rigid severity of the glaring snow-covered houses and the tree covered in frost, which stand out against the sombre sky. The painting is datable around 1670.
Provenance: Sir E. H. Scott Collection, London.

274 FISHING VESSELS IN A STORMY SEA.
Canvas, 49 × 61 cm.

Ruisdael began painting seascapes and flat landscapes only late in life. This canvas is dated in the late sixties and reveals the painter's fascination for the force of the sea and the natural elements.
Provenance: Count Henri Greffulhe Collection, Paris.

RUYSDAEL, Salomon van.

* probably between 1600 and 1603 in Naarden
\+ 1670 in Haarlem.
Salomon was the younger brother of Isaac van Ruisdael and therefore uncle of Isaac's son Jacob. No documents regarding his artistic education are known, although stylistically he is recognizable as a pupil of Esaias van de Velde and as influenced by Pieter Molyn and Jan van Goyen. Around 1630 he developed his own style and began to paint landscapes in brown, grey and green tones, gradually choosing warmer and more luminous colours. He varied his subjects, representing shore landscapes, seascapes, ferries, 'amusements on the ice' and still lifes.

275 RIVER LANDSCAPE WITH FISHERMEN.
Oak, 51.5 × 83.5 cm.
Signed and dated on the boat to the right: 'S. vR. 1645'.

Salamon van Ruysdael's development towards a mature landscape style, which began about 1647, is illustrated here in the accentuation of light and shade contrasts in the grove to the left, and in the slender trees rising from the brushwood clearly outlined against the limpid sky.

275 A RETURN OF THE FISHERMEN.
Oak, 46 × 63 cm.
Signed and dated lower left: 'S. vR. 1660' [or 1666].

The painting is a fine example of the late style of Salomon van Ruysdael, when he created his poetic compositions with groups of sailing boats on still water in the evening sunlight.
Provenance: Sir E. H. Scott Collection, London.

276 VIEW OF ALKMAAR FROM THE SEA.
Oak, 36 × 32.5 cm.
Signed on the sailing boat in the foreground: 'S vR'.

Around 1650 Salomon van Ruysdael painted various small vertical marine pieces, harmonious well-balanced compositions in silvery tones, following a development started by Jan Porcellis and Jan van Goyen. In the background is the town of Alkmaar, with the Late Gothic church of St. Laurentius.
Provenance: Joseph Block Collection, Berlin.

SALINI, Tommaso, called Mao.

* 1575 in Rome + ca. 1625 in Rome.
A pupil of Giovanni Baglione and influenced by Caravaggio, his religious compositions were close to Late Mannerism in style. He was one of the first followers of Caravaggio to paint still lifes.

277 A YOUNG PEASANT WITH FLASK.
Canvas, 99 × 73 cm.

The representation of vegetables in the foreground confirms Salini's excellence as a still-life painter. The image of the young peasant, full of life, differs from the static figures in Salini's early altarpieces. The painting is to be dated in the last years of the master's life.
Provenance: Salavin Collection, Paris.

SAENREDAM, Pieter Jansz.

* 1597 in Assendelft + 1665 in Haarlem.
From 1609 he lived almost continuously in Haarlem, and in 1623 was admitted as a master to the Guild of St. Luke. He was chiefly a painter of architecture, particularly of church interiors. Stechow called him 'the greatest genius of realism among all the Dutch masters of the seventeenth century'.

277 B FACADE OF THE CHURCH OF SAINT MARY IN UTRECHT.
Wood, 65 × 51 cm.
Signed and dated on top of the tower: 'P. S. fecit 1662'.

This architectural subject testifies to the high quality of the master's drawing and colouring. The apparent simplicity of the composition is based on accurate studies and on a number of precise drawings máde from different angles.
Provenance: F. Jurgens Collection, Egham, Surrey.

SCOREL, Jan van.

* 1495 in Schoorl + 1562 in Utrecht.
After attending the Latin school in Alkmaar, he became a pupil of Cornelis Buys the Elder and around 1512 was apprenticed to Jacob Cornelisz in Amsterdam. In 1518 he undertook a long journey first to Nüremberg to meet Albrecht Dürer, and then to Carinthia, Venice and Jerusalem. On his return he went to Rome, where the newly elected Dutch Pope, Hadrian VI, appointed him curator of antiquities. After the death of the Pope in 1523 he returned to Holland, settling in 1524 in Utrecht, where he was first vicar and later canon. He spent the period from 1527 to 1530 in Haarlem, with Maerten van Heermskerck as his pupil. The first universally formed painter of the Northern Netherlands, art to him not only represented the painter's handicraft, but also a significant spiritual activity. Scorel contributed greatly to the introduction of Italian High Renaissance painting in the Netherlands.

280 MADONNA AND CHILD WITH TWO DONORS.
Oak, 55 × 76 cm.

The representation of the Madonna reveals the influence of Raphael, whose work Scorel had studied while in Rome. The Virgin is holding narcissi, a Marian symbol. The female donor appears on the right, the male donor on the left. Datable around 1527-1529.

SEBASTIANO DEL PIOMBO (Sebastiano Luciani).

* around 1485 in Venice + 1547 in Rome.
He began painting around 1500, and probably learned his craft in the workshop of Giovanni Bellini. Later he worked with Giorgione, with whom he remained in close contact until the latter's death. In 1511 he left Venice in order to decorate a room of the Villa Farnesina with frescoes. In close touch with Raphael, he accomplished some of his best portraits under his influence. From 1516 onward he became a friend of Michelangelo. In 1531 Pope Clement VII appointed him keeper of the Papal Seal, hence his nickname 'del Piombo'. In the last decade of his life he limited his activity completely to portrait painting and became the most appreciated portraitist of his time in Rome.

281 PORTRAIT OF FERRY CARONDOLET
WITH HIS SECRETARIES.
Poplar, 112.5 × 87 cm.

The sitter is identified by the inscription on the letter in his hand: Ferry Carondolet, Archdeacon of Besançon, counsellor of the Emperor and ambassador in Rome from 1510 to 1512, years during which this portrait must have been painted. From the beginning of the seventeenth century it was considered a work of Raphael and only in the nineteenth century was the portrait recognized as one of the most significant works by Sebastiano.
Provenance: Duke of Grafton Collection,
Euston Hall, Suffolk.

SEGHERS, Herkules.

* 1589 or 1590 in Haarlem + before 1639 in The Hague.
A pupil of Gillis van Coninxloo, he lived in Amsterdam, Haarlem, Utrecht and The Hague in poverty and wretchedness. As a painter and etcher he chose landscapes as his main subject. The particular value of his etchings is due to the fact that they were engraved with a new technique developed by Seghers himself, a first step towards modern etchings in colour. Seghers worked entirely alone, creating impressive landscape paintings particularly appreciated by Rembrandt, owner of some of these works.

281 A LANDSCAPE WITH MERCENARIES.
Canvas on wood, 35.5 × 54 cm.

In the landscapes of Seghers, figures are completely absent or have only a secondary importance. According to Bode, the atmosphere of the paintings reflected the melancholic temperament of the artist and his tendency to loneliness.

SEGNA DI BONAVENTURA.

Sienese school. Documented for the first time in Siena in 1298. Together with Ugolino da Siena he was one of the best known pupils of Duccio, although not one of the most gifted. He was head of a flourishing workshop and worked for many churches in the surroundings of Siena. His death is mentioned in a document of 1331.

282 MADONNA WITH SAINTS, ANGELS AND DONOR.
Poplar, gabled, 41 × 25 cm.

SEMITECOLO, Nicoletto.

He lived in the second half of the fourteenth century and is first documented in Venice in 1353. In 1367 he painted in churches in Padua. Inspired by the grand and solemn art of Paolo Veneziano and influenced by Guariento, he formed his own effective, narrative and true Gothic style.

284 CORONATION OF THE VIRGIN.
Poplar, 87 × 53 cm.
Inscription and date: '1355'.

Suida, Coletti, Berenson and Pallucchini agreed in attributing the painting to Semitecolo. 'The author of this panel shows the immediate influence of Paolo Veneziano, but succeeds in expressing in a personal and original way a high level of gracefulness and refinement of form, which became the essential characteristics of Semitecolo's style.' (Pallucchini).

SIBERECHTS, Jan.

* 1627 in Antwerp + around 1700-1703 in London.
Nothing is known regarding the artistic education and background of the painter. In 1648-1649 he appears as a master of the Guild of St. Luke in Antwerp; in 1672 he is documented for the last time in Antwerp and around 1674 he went to England. His early work, from 1653 to about 1660, is closely related to Italianizing Dutch artists like J. Both, K. Dujardin and J. Asselijn, and suggests Siberechts' presence in Rome. His favourite subjects are herdsmen or peasant women with cattle, peasant carts or coaches fording shallow water, or shepherdesses resting among their flocks. In England Siberechts painted panoramic bird's-eye views of country houses for English noblemen.

285 THE FORD.
Canvas, 63 × 55 cm.
Signed and dated on the top stone on the left: 'J. siberechts. Anno 1661'.

The painting shows the graceful quality of Siberechts' landscapes, illustrating the peaceful atmosphere of the idyllic way of life in the country. The colours are bright and forceful and the garments stand out from the green of the vegetation.
Provenance: Donald Boylon Collection, Boston.

SOLARIO, Andrea.

* 1473-1474 in Milan + around 1520 in Milan.
Probably a pupil of his brother, the sculptor Cristofero Solario, with whom around 1490 he went to Venice. There he developed his own style inspired by Giovanni Bellini and Antonello da Messina. After his return to Milan he was strongly influenced by Leonardo. Solario was an excellent protraitist.

286 PORTRAIT OF A YOUNG MAN.
Poplar, 30.3 × 27.8 cm.

Waagen attributed the portrait to Giovanni Bellini, Suida ascribed it to Solario and Berenson listed it as an early work by the master. Today the last mentioned attribution is generally accepted, although Lotto has also been suggested as the painter of this portrait.
Provenance: Lord Leconfield Collection,
Petworth Park, Sussex.

STEEN, Jan.

* 1626 in Leiden + 1679 in Leiden.
Son of a brewer, Jan Steen received his artistic education between 1640 and 1646, with Knüpfer in Utrecht, Adriaen van Ostade in Haarlem and Jan van Goyen in The Hague as his teachers. In 1648 he became a founder member of the Guild of St. Luke in Leiden. In 1649, when resident in The Hague, he married Margaretha van Goyen, daughter of his former master. He was not only active as a painter but also as a brewer and inn keeper. After stays in Delft, Warmond and Haarlem, he returned to Leiden following the death of his wife in 1669. The majority of his paintings show a mischievous sense of humour and a true zest for life. On account of his inexhaustible imagination and his great talent as a painter, Jan Steen became one of the leading genre painters of the seventeenth century.

287 SELF-PORTRAIT WITH A LUTE.
Oak, 55.5 × 44 cm.
Signed bottom right: 'JSteen'.

Portraits and self-portraits by Jan Steen are rare and generally have also a symbolic meaning. The painter represents himself dressed up in romantic-gallant costume in the role of a successful lover. The smiling face with the fat double chin and the untended locks contrast with the rich drapery, suggesting the artist's subtle sense of irony.
Provenance: Earl of Northbrook Collection, London.

288 VILLAGE WEDDING.
Oak, 62 × 49 cm.
Signed bottom right: 'JSteen'.

Closely related to the wedding procession dated 1653 in the Six Collection, the painting may be dated around 1650-1653. The figures are vigorously and wittily characterized. Despite the bride advancing with bent head, the solemnity of the occasion is undermined by all sorts of boisterous marginal scenes.
Provenance: D. G. van Beuningen Collection, Rotterdam.

289 TAVERN SCENE.
Canvas, 44 × 37 cm.

The painting can be interpreted in the following way: the gentleman seated at the table on the right is an elderly lover to whom the unpleasant, bent little man is trying to offer the apparently pregnant lady on the left. The man in the background is smiling derisively.
Provenance: Louis Miéville Collection, Paris.

STOMER, Matthias.

* around 1600 in Amersfoort, Netherlands
\+ after 1650 probably in Sicily.
According to church documents and other records, Stomer was in Rome in 1630, and in the following year moved to Naples, where he painted a series of five scenes of the Passion for the Capuchin church of S. Efrem Nuovo, now in the Museo Nazionale. From 1641 he is documented in Sicily, where numerous paintings of his are still preserved, particularly in Palermo, Monreale and Messina.

289 A SUPPER AT EMMAUS.
Canvas, 111 × 153 cm.
Signed bottom right on the back of the chair: 'M. Stom - fecit'.

The painting is closely related to the night scenes of Stomer's teacher, Honthorst, but has a stronger and more effective contrast of light and a more plastic appearance, probably derived from the influence of contemporary painting in Naples. Stomer's later works are even more noticeably influenced by Caravaggio's late style.
Provenance: Christian Cruse Collection, Bordeaux.

STRIGEL, Bernhard.

* around 1465-1470 in Memmingen + 1528 in Memmingen.
Son of the carver Ivo Strigel, he was the most important member of a large family of painters and sculptors whose carved altarpieces with painted wings are to be found in great number in Southern Germany and in Eastern Switzerland as far as Graubünden. His good relations with Emperor Maximilian led to important commissions, in which he demonstrated his particular gift as a painter of altarpieces and portraits.

291 ANNUNCIATION. TWO WINGS OF AN ALTARPIECE.
Pine, both 118 × 50 cm.
Left wing, verso: Virgin Annunciate.
Recto: kneeling saint with book in a landscape (carved relief).
Right wing, verso: Archangel Gabriel.
Recto: seated saint with book and wild animals in a landscape (carved relief).

Originally both panels were wings of a carved altarpiece probably commissioned for the church of St. Anthony in Memmingen. The painted sides were attributed to Bernhard Strigel by Friedländer. Hugelshofer ascribed the reliefs on the inside to Ivo Strigel, father of the painter, whereas G. Otto believed them to be works by the carver Hans Thoman, a member of Ivo Strigel's workshop.

291 A THE ANNUNCIATION TO SAINT ANNE AND SAINT JOACHIM.
Wood, 58 × 30 cm.

An angel in a light, richly-folding garment approaches the crying St. Anne with the good tidings, while St. Joachim, visible through the window in the field, learns the Annunciation, too. The panel was probably part of an altarpiece and was shortened at the bottom, as can be clearly seen from the cut-off scroll. It was dated by G. Otto around 1506-1507, when Strigel painted on the ten panels of the Anne altarpiece in Mindelheim the whole family of Saint Anne according to the Legenda Aurea.
Provenance: Robert von Hirsch Collection, Basle.

STROZZI, Bernardo.

* 1581 in Genoa + 1644 in Venice.
Strozzi was a pupil of the Sienese Pietro Sorri in Genoa from 1595 to 1597. Shortly after his apprenticeship he entered the Capuchin convent of S. Barbara in Genoa, leaving it in 1610 for active priesthood. In 1630 he went to Venice and was soon recognized as the leading master. Particularly on account of his late work in Venice, he became the renewer of Venetian painting, at the time stagnating in the Mannerism of the Academicians and of Palma the Younger.

293 SAINT CECILIA.
Canvas, 150 × 110 cm.

Fiocco dated the painting as belonging to Strozzi's Genoese period, between 1623 and 1625. A companion piece, 'St. Catherine', is in the Wadsworth Atheneum in Hartford. A second version of the 'St. Cecilia' with slight variations is to be found in the Rockhill Nelson Art Gallery in Kansas City.
Provenance: Italico Brass Collection, Venice.

SWEERTS, Michael.

* 1624 in Brussels + 1664 in Goa, India.
The son of a Brussels merchant, nothing is known about his artistic education until 1646, when he is mentioned for the first time in the parish archives of S. Maria del Popolo in Rome. He was in Rome until 1654, influenced by Caravaggism. In 1656 he was active in Brussels; in 1658 he moved to Amsterdam and in 1661 joined a group of French missionaries bound for India, as a lay-brother.

295 SOLDIERS PLAYING DICE.
Canvas, 87.5 × 74 cm.

The scene must have been painted in Rome in 1652, judging from a comparison with the 'Backgammon Players' by Sweerts in the Rijksmuseum in Amsterdam. The introspective figures, the light coming from one side, the particular accentuation of certain details against the dark background and the melancholy atmosphere are elements characteristic of the artist.

TENIERS, David the Younger.

* 1610 in Antwerp + 1690 in Brussels.
A pupil of his father, David Teniers the Elder, he was admitted as a master to the Antwerp Guild in 1632-1633. He married the daughter of Jan Brueghel the Elder in 1637; in 1651 he moved to Brussels as court painter to the Archduke Leopold Wilhelm. As Adrian Brouwer before him, Teniers painted peasant scenes which differed, however, from the work of Brouwer in refinement of colour and brushwork. David Teniers was one of the most successful genre painters of the seventeenth century in the Southern Netherlands.

297 LANDSCAPE WITH FARMHOUSES.
Oak, 16 × 20 cm.
Signed below in the middle: 'D. T.'.

Figures of peasants near huts in a landscape was a theme represented by Teniers in numerous variations, mainly in small size.

297 A THE GREEN CAP.
Oak, 41.5 × 39.8 cm.
Signed bottom right: 'D. Teniers'.

At the beginning of the seventeenth century the habit of smoking the pipe reached Europe from England, quickly becoming very popular despite its being forbidden by Church and State. Scenes with smokers, a favourite subject in Flemish painting of the period, had already been represented by Brouwer and were taken over by Teniers. This painting was executed around 1637, followed by various representations of smokers in the same interior. Provenance: Baron de Rothschild Collection, Paris.

TERBORCH, Gerard.

* 1617 in Zwolle + 1681 in Deventer.
He was a pupil of his father and of the landscape painter Pieter Molyn in Haarlem. From 1635 to 1640 he travelled in England, Italy, Spain and France and in 1646 he accompanied the Dutch envoy to the peace congress of Münster, where he painted miniature portraits of many of the diplomats present there as well as his famous picture of the 'Ratification of the Treaty of Münster'. In 1645 he settled in Deventer, where especially in domestic scenes he developed his own individual style, showing great psychological subtlety and an unsurpassed refinement in the rendering of materials and costumes.

298 PORTRAIT OF A LADY SITTING AT A TABLE.
Canvas, 58 × 46 cm.
Signed and dated on the lower part of the chair: 'G. T. Borch 1658'.

Terborch dedicated himself particularly to portrait painting around 1660. He preferred full-length figures, rendering in detail the costumes and the posture of his models, as seen in this painting.
Provenance: Germanisches Museum, Nuremberg.

299 PORTRAIT OF A MAN AGED 42.
Copper; oval field on a rectangular plate, 24 × 19 cm.
Signed and dated centre right: 'AETATIS 42. 1652'.

300 PORTRAIT OF A WOMAN AGED 30.
Copper; oval field on a rectangular plate, 24 × 19 cm.
Signed and dated centre left: 'AETAT. 30 GTB 1652'.

Both paintings are companion pieces. According to Gudlaugsson, the year 1652 on the two portraits does not correspond to the year when they were painted, but rather to the date when Terborch reworked them. They are early works by the master, probably executed around 1640. Terborch also reworked the sitters' costumes according to the fashion of 1652. Differently shaped collars of the earlier versions are still visible.

300 A PORTRAIT OF A MAN READING A LETTER.
Canvas, 47.5 × 39 cm.

Gudlaugsson dated the painting around 1675, in the late period of the master's activity, on account of the hairstyle. In this period Terborch no longer represented his figures against an empty space as in his early portraits, but in homely interiors.
Provenance: H. E. ten Cate Collection, Oldenzaal, Holland.

TIEPOLO, Giambattista.

* 1696 in Venice + 1770 in Madrid.
Tiepolo received his first artistic education from Gregorio Lazzarini, developing his own style independently under the influence of Piazzetta and Sebastiano Ricci. Before long he made a name for himself as one of the most appreciated Venetian painters, receiving commissions in Italy and abroad. Together with his sons Giovanni Domenico and Lorenzo, in 1750 he went to Würzburg in order to decorate with frescoes the residence of the prince-bishop. After his return to Venice he accomplished commissions for Louis XV of France and George III of England. Invited to Madrid by Charles III of Spain in 1761, he set out in 1762. Until 1766 he painted frescoes for the king and subsequently numerous other commissions until he died suddenly in Madrid in 1770. The great quantity of frescoes, oil paintings, drawings and etchings document his exceptional creative activity as the leading Venetian master of the eighteenth century.

301 A WAY TO GOLGOTHA.
Canvas, 79 × 86 cm.

The painting belongs to a series of eight scenes from the Passion of Christ, probably later used by Tiepolo as a model for the central panel of his large triptych with Christ carrying the Cross, painted for the church of S. Alvise in Venice and closely related to the 'Way to Golgotha'.
Provenance: Canto Collection, Milan.

301 THE DEATH OF HYACINTHUS.
Canvas, 287 × 235 cm.

This painting, commissioned by Count Schaumburg, was executed when Tiepolo was active in Würzburg in 1752-1753. The master also used several details from this painting in the frescoes on the ceiling of the Würzburg Residence. Illustrated is one of the Metamorphoses by Ovid, which describes how Hyacinthus died in the discus match with Apollo as jealous Zephyr deviated Apollo's discus. From the blood of Hyacinthus' wound Apollo made bloom a hyacinth, seen on the right. Curiously, Tiepolo replaced the discus with the racket of the new game of tennis.
Provenance: Prince Schaumburg-Lippe of
Bückeburg Collection, Schloss Stadthagen.

TIEPOLO, Giandomenico.

* 1727 in Venice + 1804 in Venice.
Giandomenico, the eldest son of Giambattista Tiepolo, was trained by his father and subsequently engaged to work with him. He was not only influenced, but also overshadowed by his father, accompanying the latter on his journeys to Germany and Spain. He developed his own style only after his father's death in 1770.

302 APOTHEOSIS OF HERCULES.
Canvas, oval, 102 × 85.5 cm.

This study for a ceiling must have been executed in Spain around 1765. During this period the works of Giandomenico can hardly be distinguished from those of his father's.
Provenance: Friedrich August von Kaulbach Collection, Munich.

303 THE EXPULSION FROM THE TEMPLE.
Canvas, 104 × 195 cm.

The painting was dated by Morassi around 1760.
Provenance: M. Millron Collection, Paris.

TINTORETTO, Jacopo Robusti, called

* 1518 in Venice + 1594 in Venice.
He was the son of a silk dyer, the origin of his surname. Nothing is known about his apprenticeship. His early pictures, however, are close to works by Paris Bordone, Andrea Schiavone and Bonifazio de' Pitati, who may have been his masters. With the exception of a trip to Mantua, Tintoretto never left Venice. His commissioners were the Venetian Republic, Venetian confraternities, churches and private citizens. From 1548 onwards he executed a great number of paintings for the Scuola Grande di San Marco, with scenes from the life of the saint; in 1564 he began the decoration of the Scuola Grande di San Rocco, one of the most important cycles in Italian painting. After the fires in the Doge's Palace in 1574 and 1576, he created several paintings for its new decoration, including the 'Paradise' for the Assembly Hall of the Great Council, 7 × 22 metres, the largest painting in the world.

304 LUCRETIA AND TARQUINIUS.
Canvas, 85.5 × 101 cm.

Ovid and Livy described Lucretia's attempt to defend her virtue. Wife of the Roman nobleman Collatinus, her beauty had aroused the lust of the king's son, Sixtus Tarquinius, who shamefully abused her hospitality. Heavily overpainted in the early nineteenth century, the subject of the painting only appeared after cleaning.
Provenance: Habsburg Collection, Vienna.

304 A PARADISE.
Canvas, 152.4 × 490 cm.

The painting was only recently rediscovered and Prof. Pallucchini recognized it as the model for Tintoretto's masterpiece, the representation of Paradise in the Assembly Hall of the Great Council in the Doge's Palace. After the fire of 1576 when Guariento's frescoes were destroyed, the Senate commissioned several well-known artists, Francesco Bassano, Veronese, Palma Giovane and Tintoretto among them, to prepare designs for a new decoration. All the projects were based on the themes of Dante's Paradise, with the Trinity in the centre of Heaven surrounded by angels and saints on banks of clouds. The Senate chose the project by Veronese, but his death in 1588 before beginning his work led to the commission being given to Tintoretto, who, in 1589, presented a new project adopting some of Veronese's ideas and also respecting the wishes of the Senate. The picture in the Thyssen-Bornemisza Collection is the second of the two models by Tintoretto and the painting in the Doge's Palace still differs in some details. The first model by Tintoretto is in the Louvre.

305 PORTRAIT OF A VENETIAN SENATOR (Luigi Cornaro ?)
Canvas, 107.5 × 83 cm.

The picture was long considered a work by Titian. It is, however, a late work of Tintoretto's dated by van der Bercken between 1585 and 1590. Tintoretto's portraits of old men are particularly successful, as if each brushstroke served to render the wisdom of old age.
Provenance: Earl Spencer Collection, Althorp.

306 PORTRAIT OF A VENETIAN MAGISTRATE.
Canvas, 118.5 × 100 cm.

A considerable number of portraits of Venetian senators and magistrates was executed in Tintoretto's workshop, while kings, popes, princes and doges were portrayed by Titian. Paola Rossi has dated the painting around 1570.
Provenance: Corsini Collection, Florence.

TITIAN (Tiziano Vecellio).

* around 1477 in Pieve di Cadore near Belluno + 1576 in Venice.
The controversy regarding the year of Titian's birth, suggested as around 1490 by Cook, was resolved in 1955 in favour of the earlier date after the discovery of Titian's name in the death register of S. Canciano in Venice. The entry also reports that Titian did not die of plague, as hitherto supposed, but of fever at the age of 103. Titian arrived in Venice between 1496 and 1499. He learned his craft from Gentile and Giovanni Bellini and later collaborated with Giorgione. In his early works he already reached the highest artistic level. He received commissions from the leading ruling houses of Europe as the major portrait painter of his period. In Western painting, the influence of his art corresponds to the turning point from Renaissance to Baroque.

307 MADONNA AND CHILD.
Wood, 37.5 × 31 cm.
Signed on the footstool: 'TITIANUS'.

As probably the smallest of all Titian's paintings, dating is difficult. Suida proposed a date around 1525-1530; Hendy dated it around 1540 or later.
Provenance: Earl Cowper Collection, Panshanger, Hertfordshire.

308 PORTRAIT OF ANTONIO ANSELMI.
Canvas, 76 × 63.5 cm.

The sitter was identified by Rintelen on account of an old inscription on the back. The inscription reads: '[Ant]onius. Anselmus. ann. 38/1550/ [T]itianus F.' Anselmi was the secretary of Cardinal Pietro Bembo, a friend of Titian, twice portrayed by him.
Provenance: Von Dirksen Collection, Berlin.

309 PORTRAIT OF DOGE FRANCESCO VENIER.
Canvas, 113 × 99 cm.

Francesco Venier was elected doge in 1554 and died in 1556. In this period Titian, as successor of Gentile Bellini, was the official painter of the Venetian Republic and had to portray every new doge for the frieze of portraits in the Senate Chamber in the Doge's Palace. The portrait in the Thyssen-Bornemisza Collection is probably the preparatory study for the larger portrait in the Palace.
Provenance: Prince Trivulzio Collection, Milan.

310 SAINT JEROME IN THE WILDERNESS.
Canvas, 137 × 97 cm.

The painting is a later version of the 'St. Jerome' in the Brera in Milan, executed twenty years earlier. The extreme simplicity and the concentration on the essential is typical of the master's late style.
Provenance: S. E. W. Browne Collection, London.

TURA, Cosmé.

* around 1430 in Ferrara + 1495 in Ferrara.
Nothing is known about his artistic education. From 1452 to 1456 he was in Padua, meeting Donatello and Mantegna, and probably studying Venetian painting before settling in Ferrara as court painter to the Este family. Here he had the opportunity to meet Pisanello, Jacopo Bellini, Rogier van der Weyden and Piero della Francesca. He was the founder of the Ferrarese school of painting and also one of its leading representatives in the fifteenth century.

311 A SAINT JOHN THE BAPTIST IN PATMOS.
Wood, 27 × 32 cm.

The panel was listed by Longhi as a work by Tura. It was probably part of a predella and painted between 1460 and 1465.
Provenance: G. B. Gnecco Collection, Genoa.

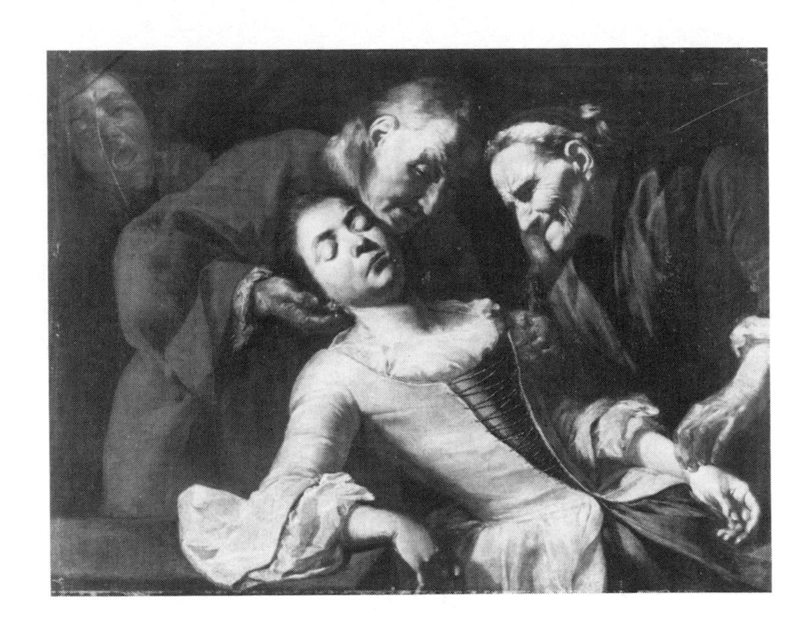

TRAVERSI, Gaspare.

* around 1732 in Naples + 1769 in Rome.
Only a few references to his life and work are found in documents. His first paintings in S. Maria dell'Aiuto in Naples, dated 1749, suggest an apprenticeship to Solimena and the influence of De Mura, Preti and Ribera. Later he went to Rome, where a considerable number of his religious paintings are still preserved. He is known, however, on account of his genre scenes, representing subjects from the stage which have an ironic or moralizing meaning. His paintings have frequently been confused with Bonito's.

311 B THE FAINTING.
Canvas, 103 × 129 cm.

This work belongs to a series of paintings by Traversi depicting moralizing scenes in his ironic way and revealing his mastery in the representation of physiognomy. Traversi's subjects are taken from the Commedia dell'Arte: the 'Innamorata', the procuress and the old lover.

UCCELLO, Paolo di Dono.

* around 1397 in Pratovecchio near Arezzo + 1475 in Florence. He is already mentioned as one of Ghiberti's apprentices in 1407, at the age of ten. In 1425 he went to Venice and worked on the mosaics in San Marco. In 1431 he returned to Florence, receiving various commissions for the decoration of the cathedral, for the cloister of S. Miniato al Monte and for S. Maria Novella. The three panels of the 'Rout of S. Romano', executed for the Medici palace in Florence, are Uccello's masterpiece. From 1465 to 1468 he was active in Urbino. Paolo Uccello's significance as one of the principal founders of Florentine Renaissance painting has only recently been acknowledged by art critics.

312 CRUCIFIXION WITH THE VIRGIN, SAINT JOHN THE EVANGELIST, SAINT JOHN THE BAPTIST AND SAINT FRANCIS.
Poplar, 46 × 67.5 cm.

The painting was probably the central panel of a predella and part of a lost altarpiece. The opinion of scholars is divided on whether this is an early or a late work. His figures express deep inner emotion and the change of colour, particularly in the green tones, appearing almost black on account of the oxidation of the copper, enhances the metaphysical quality of the painting.

UGOLINO DA SIENA.

* around 1295 + according to Vasari 1337-1347.
Few documents about Ugolino's life exist. He was probably a pupil of his father, Nerio, but his real instruction is known to have been at the hands of Duccio, one of whose most gifted and most faithful followers he was. Nevertheless, through his notable talent he found his own style, which differed considerably from his master's.

312 A CRUCIFIXION GROUP WITH MARY, SAINT JOHN AND ANGELS.
Wood, gabled, 134 × 88.5 cm.

The panel was until recently considered a work by Duccio and thought by Milanese to be the gabled top of the Sienese Maestà-altarpiece. Recent research by Parronchi and Stubblebine has definitely confirmed it as a work of Ugolino. Datable around 1325, it was originally in the monastery of San Romano near Empoli. The representation of the mourning figures under the cross, absorbed in their grief, is particularly moving.
Provenance: Toscanelli Collection, Florence.

VALCKENBORCH, Lucas van.

* around 1530 in Louvain, Brabant + 1597 in Frankfurt.
In 1560 he became member of the painters' Guild in Mechlin. A Protestant, he escaped from Antwerp first to Liège in 1566 and later to Aachen. From around 1577-1578 he was court painter to Archduke Matthias of Austria, whom he followed to Linz; from 1593 he was active in Frankfurt. Delicately executed colourful landscapes are characteristic of his work.

313 THE MASSACRE OF THE INNOCENTS.
Oak, 77.5 × 108 cm.
Signed lower right with the monogram 'LVV' and dated '1586'.

This landscape is in the style of the winter landscapes by Pieter Brueghel the Elder, who also painted a 'Massacre of the Innocents'. The dramatic event is the focal point of Brueghel's representation, whereas the figures in Valckenborch's painting appear as a colourful pictorial decoration. He probably painted only the landscape, the figures being added by Gillis Mostaert.
Provenance: Laroche Collection, Mülhausen.

VALENTIN DE BOULOGNE.

* 1594 in Coulommiers (Seine-et-Marne) + 1632 in Rome.
The son of a glass painter, Valentin descended from a family of painters. In 1613 he went to Rome, where he was fascinated by the followers of Caravaggio, particularly by Manfredi. Some eminent Roman patrons provided him with a commission for an altarpiece for St. Peter's. Valentin is one of the most significant and independent followers of Caravaggio.

314 DAVID WITH THE HEAD OF GOLIATH AND TWO SOLDIERS.
Canvas, 99 × 134 cm.

A copy of this painting, one of the most expressive and certainly most cruel creations by Valentin, is to be found in the Wallraf-Richartz-Museum in Cologne. The Cologne copy was taken for the original until in 1943 Longhi recognized it to be a seventeenth century copy. The painting in the Thyssen-Bornemisza Collection is datable around 1625.

VELAZQUEZ, Don Diego Rodriguez de Silva Y.

* 1599 in Seville + 1660 in Madrid.
His Portuguese father and his mother were of noble and wealthy birth, and gave their son an excellent education. At the age of twelve he entered the workshop of Francisco Herrera the Elder as an apprentice, and soon afterwards that of Francisco Pacheco, where he remained from 1613 to 1618. In 1623 he went to Madrid and painted a portrait of Philip IV, who engaged him as his court painter. At court he had the opportunity to study the royal collection, one of the finest in the world, and to meet Rubens, who became his friend. He was in Italy from 1629 to 1631 and again from 1649 to 1651. In 1652 the king appointed him privy chamberlain for merit. Velazquez represents the classic period of Spanish painting. His art, so balanced in colour and form, corresponds to the personality of the painter.

315 PORTRAIT OF MARIA ANNA OF AUSTRIA, QUEEN OF SPAIN (1634-1696; Queen 1649).
Canvas, 66 × 56 cm.

This portrait probably served as a preparatory study for 'Las Meninas', the famous portrait of the royal family in the Prado in Madrid. Maria Anna of Austria was chosen as the future wife of Crown Prince Balthasar Carlos, after whose sudden death the king himself married his niece, thirty years his junior.
Provenance: Walter de Zoete Collection, London.

VELDE, Adriaen van de.

* 1636 in Amsterdam + 1672 in Amsterdam.
He was the son of the painter Willem van de Velde the Elder and brother of the painter Willem the Younger. According to Houbraken, Adriaen was a pupil of Jan Wynants in Haarlem, developing, however, his own style under the influence of Paulus Potter and Karel Dujardin. Although his favourite subjects were summer pastures, he also painted seascapes and winter landscapes as well as biblical scenes. Recognized as a fine painter of figures, he added them to pictures of contemporary landscape painters.

315 A PASTORAL SCENE.
Canvas, 46 × 60 cm.
Signed and dated lower right: 'A. V. Velde F. 1663'.

Although Adriaen van de Velde probably never went to Italy, all his pastoral scenes reflect the atmosphere and the luminosity of the south, derived from the influence of Italianizing landscape painters, particularly Karel Dujardin. His precision in the rendering of details, almost microscopic, is notable.
Provenance: Sir G. L. Holford Collection,
Dorchester House, London.

VELDE THE YOUNGER, Willem van de.

* 1633 in Leiden + 1707 in Westminster, London.
Son of the marine painter Willem van de Velde the Elder, he was a pupil of his father before being apprenticed to Simon de Vlieger. He worked with his father in Amsterdam from 1652 to 1672, when the state of war led them to move to London, where they soon entered the service of Charles II and later of James II. His best paintings belong to the years between 1650 and 1670; after his move to England his work lost its spontaneity.

316 DUTCH FLEET AT ANCHOR ON A CALM SEA.
Canvas, 72 × 101 cm.
Signed below left: 'W.v.V.'.

The coats of arms, flags and comparisons with other representations, lead to the identification of the three great men-of-war as: the 'Vrede' of Amsterdam, the 'Eendracht' of Rotterdam and probably the 'Oosterwijk' of Amsterdam, proof that the painting represents the Dutch fleet under Vice-Admiral Jacob van Wassenaer-Obdam, lying at anchor off Goeree, on the Guinea coast of West Africa, in the autumn of 1664. The fleet protected Dutch merchant-ships against the English. Willem van de Velde the Elder made the drawings in situ and his son executed the painting. The picture belongs to the artist's best period, around 1664-1665.
Provenance: Baron Cassel van Doorn Collection.

VERMEER VAN HAARLEM, Jan the Elder.

* 1628 in Haarlem + 1691 in Haarlem.
At first his landscape painting was close to Jacob von Ruisdael, but later he was influenced by Philips Koninck. A direct and natural rendering of the Dutch landscape with its wide vistas marks his major works.

318 VIEW OF HAARLEM.
Canvas, 67 × 86 cm.

Vermeer based this landscape on the 'Haarlempjes' by Jacob Ruisdael, especially for the rendering of the bleaching fields in the centre. On the dune in the foreground a painter is sitting; in the background the church of St. Bavo in Haarlem can be seen. The painting is limited to a naturalistic reproduction of the landscape without the dramatic atmosphere of Ruisdael's works, and is to be dated towards the end of the 1660's.
Provenance: Fred Brunswick Collection, Berlin.

VERONESE, Paolo Caliari called

* 1528 in Verona + 1588 in Venice.
He was an apprentice of Antonio Badile in Verona. In 1553 he moved to Venice, where he executed a number of commissions for the Doge's Palace, particularly after the fire of 1576, as well as for the decoration of churches and villas in Venice and its surroundings. He not only painted numerous pictures on canvas, but also frescoes, an exception among Venetian Renaissance painters. His style tends towards the classical and the decorative, due to his collaboration with important architects of the period, such as Sansovino and Palladio.

319 ANNUNCIATION.
Canvas, 110 × 86.5 cm.

Painted around 1560, the picture is the earliest of four versions of the Annunciation by Veronese. The lapdog is a typical detail of the master, also present in the 'Portrait of a Young Lady' (cat. no. 320).

320 PORTRAIT OF A YOUNG LADY WITH LAPDOG.
Canvas, 105 × 79 cm.

The painting probably represents a member of the Muselli family of Verona. Various works by Veronese were to be found in the Muselli Collection and the portrait is listed as number 1 in the catalogue of 1662. The painting is considered one of the finest of the rare female portraits by Veronese. Suida dated it around 1560, Hadeln and Van Marle proposed a date around 1570.
Provenance: Wynn Ellis Collection, London.

VIGOROSO DA SIENA (?).

Painter of the Tuscan school, in 1276 he became a citizen of Siena, where he is documented again in 1292. The polyptych signed 'VIGOROSUS DE SENA' in the Perugia Museum reveals the influence of Guido da Siena and Cimabue.

321 TRIPTYCH.

Madonna and Child with eight scenes from the Life of Christ and the Annunciation.
Poplar, 79 × 101 cm.

Central panel: Madonna and Child; in the spandrels right and left, Angel and Virgin of the Annunciation.

Left wing: Announcement to the Shepherds and Birth of Christ; Circumcision; Transfiguration (Christ between Elijah and Moses); Christ before Pilate.

Right wing: Christ on Cross; Christ as gardener; Ascension; five saints, probably St. Clare, St. Francis, St. John the Baptist, a bishop saint and a female saint.

The attribution of the triptych to Vigoroso is disputed. Garrison attributed the triptych to the so-called 'Master of the Haniel-Tabernacle', a Venetian painter active between 1320 and 1330. Pallucchini also put the date of the triptych in the second quarter of the fourteenth century, although he pointed out a Riminese influence in the paintings.
Provenance: Langton Douglas Collection, London.

VITALE DA BOLOGNA.

* around 1308-1309 in Bologna + 1361.
A painter of the school of Bologna, he was also active as a woodcarver and miniaturist. The influence of the Lorenzetti brothers and stylistic elements of Riminese masters are noticeable in his work. His frescoes in the church of Mezzaratta belong to the most significant examples of Bolognese painting of the fourteenth century.

322 CRUCIFIXION.
Poplar, 93 × 51 cm.

The attribution of the panel to Vitale da Bologna is generally accepted. According to Gnudi it is a masterpiece from Vitale's best period and the model for the Crucifixion in the Johnson Collection in Philadelphia.

VIVARINI, Bartolomeo.

* around 1432 in Murano + after 1491.
He was an apprentice in the workshop of his elder brother, Antonio, with whom he also later worked. He was influenced by the Paduan school of painting and particularly by Mantegna. The most productive member of this family of painters, after 1462 he became the master of his own flourishing workshop with numerous assistants, including his nephew Alvise Vivarini, the most gifted member of the family.

323 SAINT JOHN THE BAPTIST.
Poplar, 48.5 × 33.5 cm.

The attribution of the panel to Alvise Vivarini was accepted by Van Marle, Fleischman and Pallucchini, whereas according to Godfrey and to Berenson it is a painting by Bartolomeo Vivarini.
Provenance: Joseph Spiridon Collection, Paris.

VLIEGER, Simon de.

* around 1600 in Rotterdam + 1653 in Weesp.
Vlieger's importance derives primarily from his seascapes. The influence of his master, Willem van de Velde, was decisive, although he did not follow the latter's preference for the objective, realistic rendering of ships, preferring to capture the atmospheric quality of water and a cloudy sky, as clearly illustrated in our painting.

323 A LIGHTNING OVER THE SEA.
Oak, 41.5 × 54.5 cm.
Signed on the pole in the water: 'S. de Vlieger'.

VOS, Cornelis de.

* 1584 in Hulst + 1651 in Antwerp.
He was the elder brother of Paul de Vos, the painter of animals, and brother-in-law of Frans Snyders. From 1599 to 1604 he was a pupil of David Remeeus in Antwerp. His importance derives mainly from his single and group portraits, influenced at first by Rubens and later by van Dyck. He also painted altarpieces and mythological scenes reminiscent of Rubens.

324 PORTRAIT OF ANTONIA VAN EVERSDYCK.
Oak, 122 × 92.5 cm.
Inscribed top right: 'AETATIS SUE 25 ANNO 1624'.

The sitter was identified on account of the coat of arms which also appeared as the coat of arms of the donors of a stained glass window in the Carmelite convent of Antwerp in 1624. The painter Willem Cornelisz Eversdyck, pupil of Cornelis de Vos in 1633-1634, also belongs to the Eversdyck family. The portrait of the husband which was certainly the companion piece to this portrait has not yet been traced.
Provenance: Gaston Neumans Collection, Paris.

VROOM, Cornelis Hendricksz.

* 1591 in Haarlem + 1661 in Haarlem.
He is considered one of the most important Dutch landscape painters prior to Ruisdael. According to Rosenberg, his activity is to be divided into three periods: the first (about 1620-1630) under the influence of Elsheimer, while in the second (about 1630-1650) he turned independently towards wood scenes, developing a new variation of Dutch landscape painting; the last period betrays a strong dependence on Jacob van Ruisdael.

324 A ON THE EDGE OF THE WOOD.
Oak, 15 × 21 cm.

The rare works of this delicate painter of small size pictures, whose particular aim was the rendering of the gracious and the intimate, were already highly appreciated during his lifetime.

VOUET, Simon.

* 1590 in Paris + 1649 in Paris.
He learned his craft from his father, Laurent Vouet, and was already a successful portraitist at an early age. In 1612 he went to Italy, first to Venice and later to Rome. After an absence of fifteen years he was recalled to France by Louis XIII and commissioned to decorate the royal residences, and to make pastel portraits of the courtiers, designs for the Gobelin tapestries and altarpieces. He owed his name, wealth and influence on the young painters of France to his indefatigable creativity.

325 THE RAPE OF EUROPA.
Canvas, 179 × 141.5 cm.

The painting represents one of the Metamorphoses of Ovid. Jupiter, as a bull, abducts the king's daughter across the sea. It is one of the best preserved examples of the art of Vouet and is probably part of the numerous decorations he painted for elegant Parisian residences; it is to be dated around 1640 on account of its style. This work reveals the artist's gift for the decorative, which made him a born wall painter; his sensitive use of luminous colour, an inspiration to the painting of the eighteenth century, is also evident.
Provenance: O'Campo Collection, Paris.

WATTEAU, Antoine.

* 1684 in Valenciennes + 1721 in Nogent-sur-Marne.
Throughout his life Watteau was oppressed by poverty. Sent by his father as an apprentice to the painter Albert Gérin in Valenciennes, he had to leave him as his father refused to pay his board. At the age of 16 or 17 he went to Paris, and in order to earn his living he worked for several years in a workshop where paintings were copied in series. Finally he met his future teacher, Claude Gillot. He began to be successful and was appointed Professor at the Academy. In 1719 he went to London, where he received a number of commissions before returning to Paris mortally ill in 1720, dying there of tubercolosis the following year. Although over two thirds of Watteau's work is missing or destroyed, the few paintings and drawings preserved point to his being one of the greatest geniuses in the history of painting.

325 B THE REST (La Halte).
Canvas, 32 × 42.5 cm.

After many years in Paris, Watteau returned to his hometown Valenciennes for a while in 1710. He found it crowded with mercenaries returning from Malplaquet and created 10 paintings and a number of drawings of groups of mercenaries, among which the painting in the Thyssen-Bornemisza Collection. Like all his representations of mercenaries and peasants, this is a typical example from the beginning of his artistic career.
Provenance: Duveen Collection, New York.

325 C PIERROT CONTENT.
Canvas, 35 × 31 cm.

During his maturity Watteau created a number of representations of 'fêtes galantes'. As performances on the stage were particularly fashionable in this period, guests present at the festivals usually held in romantic spots in parks or woods frequently used to wear costumes from the Italian comedy. 'Pierrot content' is one of the earliest representations of 'fêtes galantes' by Watteau. These paintings, which appear today as images of a surrealistic, magic world, were to Watteau's contemporaries scenes taken from real life.
Provenance: Mrs Charles P. Curtis Collection, Boston.

WERTINGER, Hans.

* between 1465 and 1470 in Landshut + 1533 in Landshut.
He was a painter, glass painter and designer of woodcuts, influenced at first by Hans Mair of Landshut and later by Hans Burgkmair the Elder. After 1515 he painted a number of portraits of the Bavarian ducal family.

326 PORTRAIT OF 'RITTER CHRISTOPH'.
Pine, 113.5 × 61 cm.

The painting is a life-size portrait of the court dwarf of Philip, Bishop of Freising, Count Palatine and Duke of Bavaria. Christoph bore the title of 'Ritter', sometimes jokingly awarded to court dwarfs, as results from an inscription on the back of the panel which also gives the date of execution: 1515.
Provenance: Property of Baroness Leoni von Boyneburgh,
Vereinslazarett Wülfingerode near Sollstedt.

WEYDEN, Rogier van der.

* 1399 or 1400 in Tournai + 1464 in Brussels.
In 1427 he was a pupil of Robert Campin in Tournai together with Jacques Daret. In 1432 he left the workshop as a master, and in 1435 he is documented as town painter in Brussels, where he lived until his death. In 1450 he went to Italy. Rogier van der Weyden had many pupils and led a flourishing workshop, the influence of which was felt all over Europe. After the radiant art of Jan van Eyck, the painting of Rogier van der Weyden represents a return to spiritual and religious values.

328 MADONNA AND CHILD ENTHRONED.
Oak, 14 × 10.5 cm.

The niche of the throne and the architecture of the porch symbolize the Church. The pinnacles of the pillars are adorned with six statues of prophets. In the small arches in the upper part are represented: the Annunciation, the Visitation, the Birth of Christ, the Adoration of the Magi, the Resurrection and the Descent of the Holy Spirit, which flank the Coronation of the Virgin in the centre over the finial. The unmistakable influence of van Eyck and of Robert Campin indicate the panel as an early work, whereas the relief-like treatment of the composition points towards his later style.
Provenance: Earl of Northbrook Collection, London.

329 PORTRAIT OF A MAN.
Oak, 32 × 22.8 cm.

The sitter was thought to be either Rogier van der Weyden himself or Pieter Bladelin or Pierre del Beffremont, Count of Charny, suppositions not sufficiently proved. A date of execution around 1455 is generally accepted. Rogier composed his portraits against a monochrome background, omitting details in order to emphasize the individual features of the sitter.
Provenance: Dr Wendland Collection, Basle.

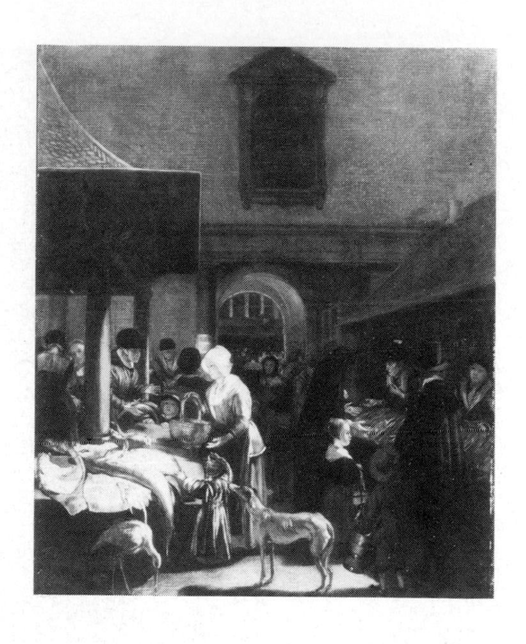

WITTE, Emanuel de.

* around 1617 in Alkmaar + 1692 in Amsterdam.
He entered the Guild of St. Luke in Alkmaar in 1636 and was later active in Rotterdam, Delft and Amsterdam. At first a painter of historical subjects, he later dedicated himself to the reproduction of church interiors, probably inspired by the perspectives painted by Carel Fabritius. He made a significant contribution to the development of the representation of interiors in Dutch painting. After settling in Amsterdam in 1650, he painted scenes from that city's commercial life, such as 'The Fish Market' and the 'Amsterdam Stock Exchange'. After 1658 documents refer to de Witte's difficulties, debts and poverty; in 1692, at the age of 75, he committed suicide.

330 THE OLD FISH MARKET ON THE DAM, AMSTERDAM.
Oak, 54.5 × 45 cm.
Signed and dated lower left: 'EDE Witt. A° 16[8?]'.

A study of the costumes date the painting around 1650. The '8' of the date is a retouch, and the last number is illegible. Topographically exact, the scene may be localized through a comparison with contemporary engravings. The painter is already here concerned about the effect of light and perspective, as can be seen by the transparent white cap of the woman and the light reflected from the fish onto her face. In his later works de Witte accentuated these effects while tending to neglect topographical precision.
Provenance: Duke of Sutherland Collection, London.

330 A INTERIOR OF A GOTHIC CHURCH.
Canvas, 52.2 × 39.5 cm.
Signed and dated under the organ to the right: 'E. de Witte 1661'.

Around 1660 de Witte attained such an expertise in the rendering of architectural elements that he began painting imaginary churches, of which this interior of a Gothic church inspired by the Oude Kerk of Amsterdam is an example.
Provenance: P. van Leeuwen Boomkamp Collection,
Hilversum.

WOLGEMUT, Michael.

* 1433 or 1434 in Nuremberg + 1519 in Nuremberg.
In 1516 Albrecht Dürer painted the impressive portrait of his former teacher at the age of 82, now in the Museum of Nuremberg. Probably Michael Wolgemut owed his artistic education to his father, Valentin Wolgemut. Around 1465 he was active in the workshop of Hans Pleydenwurff in Nuremberg, taking over the latter's workshop after his death and marrying his widow. Accurate design and meticulous execution as well as a sober simplicity mark Wolgemut's style. Numerous altarpieces, portraits and woodcut illustrations were executed in his workshop.

331 PORTRAIT OF LEVINUS MEMMINGER.
Pine, 33.5 × 23 cm.

The attribution of the portrait to Michael Wolgemut is due to W. Wenke, who was the first to recognize the similarity between the sitter and the representation of St. Vitus in the St. Catherine altarpiece in the church of St. Lawrence, Nuremberg. This altarpiece was painted by Wolgemut in 1485, probably commissioned by the Memminger family; the portrait is presumed to have been painted at the same time. The falcon pouncing upon the pheasant is an astrological symbol.
Provenance: Countess Sala Collection, Paris.

WOUWERMAN, Philips.

* 1619 in Haarlem + 1668 in Haarlem.
He was the son of Paulus Joosten Wouwerman, painter of historical subjects, from whom he probably received his first artistic education before he became a pupil of Frans Hals. In 1640 he was admitted to the painters' Guild of Haarlem and began his successful career leaving more than a thousand pictures after thirty uninterrupted years of creative activity. He was already a highly appreciated painter during his own lifetime. Horses and horsemen were the favourite subject of all his paintings.

332 HORSE AND THREE DONKEYS NEAR WATER.
Oak, 28.5 × 22.5 cm.
Signed at the bottom left with the monogram: 'Ph. W.'.

The painting is a typical example of Wouwerman's early work, with only a few animals placed in a landscape. The tonality recalls Pieter Verbeeck, the Haarlem painter of horses.
Provenance: Dr H. Wetzlar Collection, Amsterdam.

ZOPPO, Marco Ruggiero, called

* 1433 in Cento near Ferrara + 1478 in Venice.
At the age of twenty he entered Squarcione's workshop in Padua, where he was influenced by Mantegna and Donatello. In 1456 he went to Venice, studying the works of Giovanni Bellini and Bartolomeo Vivarini. After a lengthy period in Bologna he returned to Venice in 1471. He was also a gifted draughtsman and his best drawings were long attributed to Mantegna.

333 SAINT JEROME IN THE WILDERNESS.
Poplar, 38 × 28 cm.
Signed on the stone base of the cross: 'MARCO ZOPPO D.A. BONONIA'.

Ruhmer dated the painting around 1460-1470 on account of its being stylistically related to the 'Dead Christ with St. John the Baptist and St. Jerome' in the National Gallery in London. During that period Zoppo was in Bologna and was influenced by the Ferrarese school.
Provenance: Richard von Kaufmann Collection, Berlin.

ZURBARÁN, Francisco de.

* 1598 in Fuente de Cantos, Estremadura + 1664 in Madrid.
In 1614 he was sent by his father, a merchant, as apprentice to the painter Pedro Diàz de Villanueva in Seville. After qualifying as a master, he returned home and settled in Llerena in 1617. Due to his great zeal he had already made himself a name by 1629, and was invited to settle in Seville by the city fathers. In 1659 he went to Madrid on invitation of the king. Zurbarán was a friend of Velazques and was influenced by Ribera. His clear, static modelling, his simple, rigorous compositions and his intense and velvety colour scheme combine realism with an almost mystical spirituality.

335 CHRIST ON THE CROSS.
Canvas, 214 × 143.5 cm.

Twelve versions of the Crucifixion painted by Zurbarán are known to day, and the painting in the Thyssen-Bornemisza Collection is one of the earliest and most magnificent, probably executed in 1627 for the sacristy of the Dominican Monastery of St. Paul in Madrid.
Provenance: Dr M. K. Rohe Collection, Munich.

336 SAINT AGNES.
Canvas, 140 × 107 cm.
Provenance: Duke of Béjar Collection, Madrid.

336 A SAINT ELIZABETH OF THURINGIA.
Canvas, 171 × 107 cm.

Provenance: Van Horne Collection, Montreal.

Between 1630 and 1645 Zurbarán painted numerous representations of female saints which testify to his great talent as a portrait painter. They were mainly life-size single portraits of magnificent Andalusian female figures, festively dressed, often richly and fashionably adorned, set against a dark, neutral background. They were frequently used as altarpieces and were mostly painted in series and hung in church naves. A series of these portraits was also executed for the Hospital de la Sangre in Seville. Unfortunately most of them have been lost and the few preserved are favourite collectors' items.

FÜSSLI, Johann Heinrich.

* 1741 in Zurich + 1825 in London.
Ordained minister of the Evangelic Reformed Church in 1761, he was, however, primarily interested in literature and in politics rather than in religion. In 1763 he left Switzerland on account of his difficulties with the authorities caused by his radical political ideas, going to England, where he earned his living by writing articles on German and French literature as well as by drawing illustrations for his favourite authors. In 1767 Reynolds was so deeply impressed by his drawings that he advised him to dedicate himself entirely to art. Thanks to Reynold's support he stayed in Italy from 1770 to 1778, returning to London in 1779 to start his successful career as a painter. His preference for the dramatic and the horrible led him again and again to represent themes from Shakespeare and Milton.

481 D THE TOMB OF ROSICRUCIUS.
Canvas, 92 × 77 cm.

The painting was executed in 1803 and illustrates an essay of Eustace Budgell (1686-1737). Rosencreutz, founder of the Rosicrucian sect, died in 1484 and had enjoined that his writings be buried in a secret tomb with him. In Budgell's essay a man succeeds in entering the tomb: blinded by the glaring light, he discovers a man in armour who gets up at the first step of the intruder, at the second brandishes a staff, at the third breaks the lamp - the scene illustrated by Füssli. Later on the man in armour turns out to be an automaton, controlled by springs hidden under the ground.

EXHIBITED ART OBJECTS

K 1 HEAD OF BEARDED GOD.
Greek, IV century B.C. By the sculptor Bryaxis.
White marble, height 37 cm.

K 2 FEMALE HEAD.
Roman, I century A.D. Probably representing Vipsania, wife of Germanicus.
White marble, height 30 cm.

K 9 LION FROM A PORTAL (Lion of St. Mark).
Venice, middle XII century.
White marble with original patina, height 49 cm.

K 9a CORPUS CHRISTI.
Central Italy, 1st half XIII century.
Wood with original polychromy, height 180 cm.

K 12b BUST OF YOUNG WOMAN.
Gian Cristofero Romano (1470-1512).
Terracotta, height 54 cm.

K 12c MADONNA AND CHILD. Fragment.
Tino di Camaino (1285-1339).
Marble, height 34 cm.

K 13a ST. JOHN THE APOSTLE.
Clay model around 1489. Benedetto da Maiano (1442-1497).
Terracotta, height 93 cm.

K 14 MADONNA AND ANGELS.
Around 1470.
Agostino di Duccio (1418-1498).
High relief in stucco, 82 × 77 cm.

K 14a SLEEPING CUPID.
Venice, around 1540.
Bronze with original patina, length 30 cm.

K 16a ST. ANNE.
Francesco di Valdombrino (1400-1435).
Stucco on wood with original polychromy, height 150 cm.

K 18 BUST OF ST. JOHN.
Luca della Robbia (1400-1482).
White enamelled terracotta, height 37 cm.

K 18a MADONNA AND CHILD IN GARLAND OF FRUIT.
Luca della Robbia (1400-1482).
High relief, terracotta, tondo, diameter 84 cm.

K 18b STANDING BOY WITH SQUIRREL.
Luca della Robbia (1400-1482).
Polychrome enamelled terracotta, height 47.5 cm.

K 19 PAIR OF ANGEL CANDLESTICKS.
Around 1500.
Giovanni della Robbia (1469-1529).
Polychrome enamelled terracotta, height 66 and 68 cm.

K 19a TWO ANGELS IN PRAYER.
Around 1500.
Giovanni della Robbia (1469-1529).
Wall-figures, polychrome enamelled terracotta,
height, each, 98 cm.

K 19b SEATED BISHOP.
Giovanni della Robbia (1469-1529).
High relief, polychrome enamelled terracotta,
tondo, diameter 75 cm.

K 21 MADONNA AND CHILD.
Antonio Rossellino (1427-1479).
Marble, height 78 cm, width 55 cm.

K 23 THE ANNUNCIATION: two figures.
Andrea Sansovino (1460-1529).
Terracotta with original polychromy.
Virgin, height 88 cm, Angels 84 cm.

K 25 BUST OF ST. JOHN.
Florence, late XV century.
Circle of Verrocchio.
Stucco with original polychromy, height 37 cm, width 32 cm.

K 27 TWO DOOR LEAVES.
Florence, around 1540. Walnut, richly carved, height, each, 260 cm, width 65.5 cm. On the left leaf, St. Dominic, on the right leaf, a holy Pope.
From the Convent of S. Clemente in Prato, near Florence.

K 28 STANDING BOY. Bronze figure.
Italian, 1st half XVI century.
Represented as an ancient boxer with protective helmet and bandaged joints in position of defence.
Gilded Bronze, height 26.5 cm.

K 31 CYMON AND PERA.
Florence, late XVI century, attributed to Daniele da Volterra.
Terracotta, height 90 cm.

K 35 ST. SEBASTIAN.

Giovanni Lorenzo Bernini (1598-1680).
White Marble, height 99 cm.
Formerly in Palazzo Barberini, Rome.

K 36 BUST OF POPE BENEDICT XIII (+ 1730).

Pietro Bracci (1700-1773).
White Marble, height 93 cm.

K 38 TWO BUSTS OF APOSTLES.

El Greco (1541-1614).
Wood, height 45 and 48 cm.

K 39 KNEELING FEMALE SAINT.

Spanish, XVII century.
Wood with original polychromy, height 60 cm.

K 41 HEAD OF BEARDED MAN WITH CAP.

Île de France, 2nd half XIII century.
Probably from a convent near Bourges.
Limestone, height 38 cm.

K 41a SEATED SAINT.

French, around 1200.
Stone, height 125 cm.

K 42 SEATED MADONNA.

Auvergne, late XII century.
From a convent in Clermont Ferrand.
Dark vulcanic stone, height 72 cm.

K 42a KNEELING MADONNA.

Sienese master, around 1450.
Wood with original polychromy, height 63 cm.

K 43 MADONNA OF SIONVILLER.

School of Reims, executed around 1240.
Sandstone, with traces of original polychromy, height 181 cm.

K 44 MADONNA AND CHILD.

Île de France, executed around 1300-1320.
Limestone, height 155 cm.
From the Castle of Betz (Oise).

K 45 SMILING MADONNA.

Île de France, around 1320.
Softwood with original polychromy, height 101 cm.

K 46 ST. ANNE TEACHING THE VIRGIN.
Northern French, around 1360.
Oak, height 95 cm.

K 47 MADONNA AND CHILD.
Burgundian, around 1400.
Limestone, height 118 cm.
From a village church in the environs of Dijon.

K 48 STANDING FIGURE OF GUILLAUME D'AUNIERS.
Burgundian, around 1410.
White stone with traces of original polychromy, height 86 cm.
Held to be a representation of Guillaume d'Auniers, due to its provenance from Auniers near Fougeré (Maine-et-Loire).

K 54 WINTER.
Jean Antoine Houdon (1741-1828).
Plaster, coloured, height 149 cm.
Signed on the stump: 'Houdon'.

K 54a BUST OF VOLTAIRE.
Original Model.
Jean Antoine Houdon (1741-1828).
Terracotta, height 35 cm.
Signed on the left shoulder: 'J. A. Houdon'.

K 56 BUST OF THE SCHOLAR LOUIS JEAN MARIE DAUBENTON.
Around 1774.
Jean Antoine Houdon (1741-1828).
Plaster, coloured, height 65 cm.
Signed: 'J. A. Houdon'.

K 57 RELIQUARY-BUST.
Cologne, middle XIV century.
Lime with original polychromy, height 41 cm.

K 58a FEMALE SAINT.
German, XV century.
Pine with original polychromy, partially gilded, height 140 cm.

K 58b ST. FLORIAN.
School of Landshut, around 1510.
Lime, height 93 cm.

K 63 BUST OF BISHOP.
Master of Bressanone, around 1490.
Lime with original polychromy, height 36 cm.
In the former private chapel of the de Sardegna Family in Trent.

K 66 MATER DOLOROSA.
Flemish, late XV century, probably from the circle of Rogier van der Weyden.
Terracotta with original polychromy, height 61 cm.

K 70 LAMENTATION OVER DEAD CHRIST. Wall group.
Tilmann Riemenschneider (1460-1531).
Lime, height 91 cm, width 100 cm.

K 72 ST. ANNE, VIRGIN AND CHILD. Wall group.
Dutch, around 1500.
Oak, with traces of original polychromy, height 100 cm.

K 83 FEMALE SAINT.
South German, around 1730.
Wood with original gilding, height 180 cm.

K 84 TWO STANDING WINGED ANGELS.
Bavarian, around 1730.
Wood with original white patina, height without wings 120 cm.
Companion pieces, probably originally side figures of an altar-piece.

K 91a BAPTISM OF CHRIST. Ivory relief.
South Italian, XI century.
Height 16 cm, width 13.4 cm.

K 91b MADONNA ENTHRONED WITH CHILD. Fragment.
Ivory with traces of original polychromy.
France, around 1310-1320.
Height 23.3 cm.

K 91c TRIPTYCH WITH PASSION OF CHRIST.
France, around 1330.
Ivory relief with traces of original polychromy.
Height 24.6 cm, width 20 cm.

K 91d DIPTYCH WITH ADORATION OF THE MAGI, DEATH OF THE VIRGIN, CRUCIFIXION AND CORONATION OF THE VIRGIN.
France, around 1360.
Ivory relief, each wing 17.8 × 9.6 cm.

K 91e DIPTYCH WITH EIGHT SCENES FROM THE LIFE OF CHRIST: ANNUNCIATION, BIRTH OF CHRIST, ADORATION OF THE MAGI, PRESENTATION IN THE TEMPLE, FLAGELLATION, CRUCIFIXION, ENTOMBMENT AND RESURRECTION.
France or Flanders, XVI century.
In the centre, frieze with figures.
Ivory, 10 × 15.5 cm.

K 91g COMB.
German, 1st half XIV century.
Ivory, each wing 16.5 × 12.5 cm.

K 91i GROUP OF SEVEN TONDI.
Northern French or Flemish, 1st quarter XV century.
Diameter each 2.3 cm.

K 91l IVORY RELIEF OF THE HODEGETRIA. Madonna and Child.
Byzantine, X century.
Height 15.2 cm, width 11.4 cm.

K 91m STATUE OF DIANA WITH QUIVER, ARROWS AND BOW.
French (?), around 1600.
Ivory and gold enamel, height 17.3 cm.

K 107a BRONZE MORTAR.
Vincenzo Barberini, Rome, 1636.
Inscription and reliefs of the external surface.
Bronze, height 35.5 cm.

K 121a SOUP TUREEN WITH COVER AND SAUCER. 1758.
François Thomas Germain (1726-1791), goldsmith of Louis XV, Paris. One of eight tureens executed for the Tsarina Elizabeth.
Gilded silver, height 38 cm, length 46 cm, saucer 58.5 cm.

K 170a NAUTILUS CUP.
Cornelius Bellekin, 1660-1670, Amsterdam.
Mother-of-pearl with silver mounting in the shape of a swan.
Height 30 cm. Signed.

K 239 INKSTAND.
Padua, around 1550.
Bronze, height 29 cm.

K 253 RUSTIC JUG.
Italian, XVII century.
Bronze, height 23 cm.

K 312a JUG WITH CHRIST MONOGRAM.
Faience, around 1490.
Height 14.7 cm.

K 319d BRAZIER.
Venetian, 2nd half XVI century.
Gilded bronze, height 60 cm.

K 328 LARGE, RICHLY CARVED TABLE.
Florentine with Roman influence, around 1530.
Walnut, height 82 cm, length 307 cm, width 95 cm.

K 328a LARGE, RICHLY CARVED TABLE WITH SIX LEGS.
Genoa, XVII century.
Walnut, height 86 cm, length 253 cm, width 143 cm.

K 329 TABLE.
North Italian, late XVI century.
Walnut, height 80 cm, length 179 cm.

K 331 OCTAGONAL TABLE.
Florence, 2nd half XVI century.
Walnut, height 86 cm, diameter 104 cm.

K 332 OCTAGONAL TABLE.
Florence, 2nd half XVI century.
Walnut, height 84 cm, diameter 100 cm.

K 333 ROUND TABLE.
Siena, middle XVI century.
Walnut with gold edging, height 77 cm, diameter 107 cm.

K 336 CASSONE.
Siena, around 1400. With scenes painted by Taddeo di Bartolo (Siena 1362-1422).
Wood with stucco decoration, on gilded bole base.
Height 66 cm, length 164 cm, width 57 cm.

K 338 CASSONE.
Florence, early XVI century.
Walnut with light beech intarsias.
Height 68 cm, length 178 cm.

K 340 CASSONE.
Venice, late XV century.
Wood with original polychromy, height 51 cm, length 166 cm.

K 341 CASSONE.
Rome, 2nd half XVI century.
Walnut, height 76 cm, length 182 cm, width 62 cm.

K 343 FOUR STOOLS (grouped together with K 333).
Florence, beginning XVI century.
Walnut, height 102 cm, width 54 cm.

K 343a THREE ARMCHAIRS.
Venice, 1st half XVIII century..
Wood with decoration in Venetian lacquer and carved backs.
Height each 102 cm.
From the Royal Villa in Stra.

K 349 SIX ARMCHAIRS.
Spanish, 2nd half XVI century.
Walnut, height 111 cm, width 63 cm.
Original leather covering and brass studs.

K 350 TABLE.
Spanish, XVII century.
Walnut, height 80 cm, length 126 cm.

K 350a TABLE.
Spanish, XVII century.
Walnut, height 80 cm, length 131 cm.

K 352 FOLDING TABLE.
Dutch, late XVI century.
Oak, height 75 cm, diameter 88 cm.

K 353 TABLE.
Dutch, around 1600.
Oak, height 67 cm, width 62 cm.

K 353a TABLE.
Holland, XVII century.
Walnut, height 65 cm, length 71.5 cm.

K 354 FOLDING TABLE.
Dutch, around 1620.
Oak, height 69 cm, diameter 83 cm.

K 355 FOLDING TABLE.
Holland, around 1600.
Oak, height 74 cm, diameter 84 cm.

K 356 TABLE.
Flemish, around 1640.
Oak, height 72 cm, length 170 cm, width 80 cm.

K 356a BAROQUE PRIE-DIEU WITH FOLDING BACK.
German, early XVII century.
Wood with coloured leather.
Height of stool 51 cm, total height 102 cm.

K 363 CHEST.
Northern French, around 1500.
Oak, height 76 cm, length 162 cm.
Under pinnacles, figures of the twelve Apostles.

K 364 SMALL TABLE.
French, Île de France, around 1550.
Walnut, height 33.5 cm.

K 364a SMALL WRITING DESK.
François Delorme (master 1735).
Rosewood, height 80.5 cm, width 64 cm.
Signed: 'Delorme'.

K 364b CONSOLE TABLE, RICHLY DECORATED.

Pietro Pifetti (1732 appointed Royal cabinet maker at the court of Savoy).
Walnut, inlaid with ivory, mother-of-pearl and tortoise shell.
Height, 80.5 cm, width 107.5 cm, width 62 cm.

K 366 ROUND TABLE.

French, around 1550.
Walnut, height 61 cm, diameter 83 cm.

K 368 ARMCHAIR.

French, Île de France, around 1550.
Walnut, height 90 cm, width 59 cm.

K 368a LISEUSE.

French, Louis XV.
Bronze feet and edgings.
Walnut, height 71 cm, length 56 cm.

K 369 ARMCHAIR.

French, around 1570.
Height 120 cm, width 65 cm.
On the back, relief of a warrior.

K 372a TWO CORNER CUPBOARDS.

Bernard van Risen Burgh (of Dutch origin, active in Paris middle XVIII century).
Rosewood, height 96.5 cm, width 86.5 cm.
Signed: 'B.V.R.B. JME'.

K 373a TWO CORNER CUPBOARDS WITH MARBLE TOP.

Pierre Harry Mewesen (ebonist of Scandinavian origin, active in Paris around 1766).
Rosewood with bronze decorations, height 84 cm, width 64 cm.

K 383 GOTHIC COFFER.

South German or Tyrolian, around 1480.
Oak, height 195 cm, width 83 cm.

K 384 GOTHIC CUPBOARD.

South Tyrol, around 1500.
Cembra wood, height 112 cm, width 189 cm.

K 389 LONGCASE CLOCK.

Gerrit Ter Vooren, Amsterdam, around 1720.
Veneered oak, bronze figures on top, height 285 cm.
Signed on dial: 'Gerrit Ter Vooren Amsteldam'.

K 391 TABLE.
French, Lyons, around 1570, Italian model.
Walnut, height 81 cm, width 139 cm.

K 398a LARGE 'CASSAPANCA'.
Tuscany, middle XVI century.
Walnut with carvings.
Height with footstool 70 cm, length 308 cm.

K 399 'CASSAPANCA'.
Florence, around 1550.
Walnut, height 106 cm, width 256 cm.

K 407a CHEST OF DRAWERS.
Around 1780.
Adam Weisweiler (ebonist in Paris, born in Neuwied).
Mahogany, rosewood with coloured intarsias on oak.
Original white marble top. Impressed: 'A. Weisweiler JME'.
Height 88.5 cm, width 100 cm, depth 47 cm.

K 473 RENAISSANCE WARDROBE.
Italian, middle XVI century.
Walnut, height 102 cm, width 104 cm.

K 484 BENCH.
Dutch, around 1600.
Oak, height 54 cm, length 199 cm.

K 509 TALLBOY.
Northern French, around 1530.
Oak, height 152 cm, width 139 cm.

K 519 SIDEBOARD.
Venice, around 1550.
Walnut, height 102 cm, width 138 cm, width 87 cm.
Decorated with female-headed herms at corners.

K 522a CUVILLIÉS TABLE.
François de Cuvilliés (1695-1768).
Gilt wood with marble top.
Height 71 cm, length 116 cm.

K 585 FRAGMENT OF TAPESTRY WITH DONOR IN PRAYER.
Franconian, around 1430.
Wood and silk, 89 × 55 cm.
The fragment belongs to a tapestry with the representation of the Trinity in the Stieglitz Museum, Leningrad. Close to the donor is the coat of arms of the Duke of Schwarzenburg.

K 587 TAPESTRY WITH THE PORTRAIT OF MARTIN LUTHER.

Thuringia, middle XVI century.
Heinrich von der Hohenmuel and Seger Bombeck, after an engraving by Lucas Cranach the Elder.
Wool and gold, 130 × 108 cm.

K 589a BATTLE OF ANIMALS. Gobelin.

French, around 1732.
This Gobelin is the fifth of a series entitled 'Les Indes' executed after paintings by Albert van der Eckhout. Presented by Prince Maurice of Nassau to Louis XIV.
Wool and silk, 327 × 277 cm.

K 591 ANTEPENDIUM.

St. Martin, St. John the Baptist and St. Hugh standing in a landscape. In the background the Tarragona-La Luna coat of arms.
Eastern France, around 1420.
Wool, 81 × 235 cm.

K 596a ANTEPENDIUM WITH LAMENTATION.

Ferrara, around 1490, after a design by Cosimo Tura (1432-1495).
Wool with gold thread, 97 × 206 cm.

K 664a FRAGMENT OF PRAYER RUG WITH HIBISCUS FLOWERS.

Indian, XVII century.
Executed during the reign of Emperor Moghul Jahangir.
Silk, 124.5 × 90 cm.

K 664b KASCHGAR CARPET.

East Turkestan, XVII century.
Silk, silver and gold thread, 222 × 394 cm.

K 669a BÉHAGUE-SANGUSZKO CARPET.

Persian, early XVII century.
Silk, wool and cotton, 273 × 528 cm.
From the Countess de Béhague Collection, Paris.

K 669b THE SO-CALLED HOLBEIN TAPESTRY.

Uschak, XVII century.
Wool, 125 × 175 cm.

K 714 TOMB STELE.

Japanese, XVII century, Genroku period.
Grey limestone, height 103 cm.

K 720 ANCIENT COLUMN.

Roman, II-III century. A.D.
Withe Marble, height 123 cm.

K 721 TWO CANDELSTICKS.

XII century.
From the church of S. Maria Maggiore in Rome.
White marble with mosaic, height each 24 cm.

K 722 MARBLE CANDELABRUM ON PEDESTAL WITH TWO PUTTI.

Western German, probably Mainz, around 1790.
Close to the works of the sulptor Johann Sebastian Pfaff (1747-1794).

K 740 SMALL BOX (on table K 350).

Spanish, XVII century.
Wood, height 14 cm, length 33 cm.
Covered in leather with painted representations of animals.

K 741 TWO COLUMNS.

Italian, around 1600.
Wood, carved, with original polychromy, height each 225 cm.

ALPHABETICAL INDEX OF THE PAINTERS